Facts at Your Fingertips 1
Rapid Recall Strategies for Number Bonds Within 20

A Photocopiable Activity Book by:
Helen Maden and Jane Lambert

Introduction

The four rules of number are the foundation of numeracy work in the Primary School. Curriculum 2000 for Mathematics details how emphasis should be placed on developing the knowledge and understanding of mental calculations, then progressing to more formal written calculations.

The National Numeracy Framework for teaching Mathematics outlines how recall of number bonds should first be taught through strategies so that children fully understand their methods rather than carrying them out 'by rote'.

This book is suitable for children in KS1 who are learning their number bonds and for children in KS2 who are consolidating this knowledge and understanding. The exercises will take your children 'Step by Step' through a tried and tested system which teaches addition and subtraction recall so that children have number bond facts 'at their fingertips'.

Other books in this series include:
Facts at Your Fingertips 2 (for multiplication and division facts)
Addition and Subtraction (using Expanded Written methods)
Multiplication and Division (using Expanded Written Methods)
Addition and Subtraction 4 Rules of Number (for compact calculation practice)

Topical Resouces publishes a range of Educational materials for use in Primary Schools and Pre-school Nurseries and Playgroups.

For latest catalogue:
Tel: 01772 863158
Fax: 01772 866153

E-Mail: sales@topical-resources.co.uk
Visit our Website: www.topical-resources.co.uk

Copyright © 2004 H.Maden & J.Lambert

Printed in Great Britain for 'Topical Resources', Publishers of Educational Materials, P.O. Box 329, Broughton, Preston, PR3 5LT by T Snape & Company Ltd, Boltons Court, Preston, England.

Typeset by Paul Sealey Illustration and Design, 3 Wentworth Drive, Thornton, England. FY5 5AR.

First Published May 2004
ISBN 1 872977 85 5

Contents

Methodology

fig.1)

$$\begin{array}{r} 297 \\ +487 \\ \hline 784 \\ \hline 1\ 1 \end{array}$$

Before a child can carry out a sum such as that shown in fig.1, he/she would need to be able to carry out 3 smaller sums (fig.2), before he/she even considered whether the figures were hundreds, tens or units.

fig.2) $7+7=$ $9+8+1=$ $2+4+1=$

If children can only count on and do not know their number bonds, this process can be extremely slow.

In early number work, children in many primary schools are taught to count and then are encouraged to 'count on'. e.g.

$5+7 \longrightarrow$ start with the bigger number 7 and
                then count on the five
        $7 \longrightarrow 8, 9, 10, 11, 12$

However if we look at the sum **5+7** again, one could argue that a quicker way (and some may argue more mathematical) would be to split the 7 into **(5+2)** and change the sum to **5+5+2**. Most children quickly know that **5+5 =10** and by showing them patterns of adding 10 to different numbers, with a small amount of practice they are able to add 10 to any 1-digit number with speed.

$5+7 \longrightarrow (5+5) +2$

If we look at sums that total 20 or less there are 221 combinations. It is of course time consuming to learn all these sums individually so we have developed a system to group sums in order to maximise learning.

Firstly, children need to know that addition is commutative (i.e. 3+10 gives the same answer as 10+3). This reduces our original 221 combinations to 105 number bonds to learn. The sums they do not need to learn are crossed out in the above chart.

By systematically teaching strategies A to M and regularly using the following work sheets in timed situations in class, children will quickly become much faster at recalling their addition and subtraction number bonds. The pages can be used as a whole sheet or cut into strips if less 'sums' are needed. The sheets can also be used for homework. This will provide re-inforcement and consolidation of the children's knowledge and understanding. Once the children are confident with a particular strategy, we have found that they enjoy being timed and subsequently set targets for improvement for themselves

There is a photocopiable certificate on the last page which can be used when a child successfully masters any strategy. *e.g. 'I Now Know How to add 10.'*

The 221 Combinations (commutative facts in brackets crossed out)

0+0	(1+0)	(2+0)	(3+0)	(4+0)	(5+0)
0+1	1+1	(2+1)	(3+1)	(4+1)	(5+1)
0+2	1+2	2+2	(3+2)	(4+2)	(5+2)
0+3	1+3	2+3	3+3	(4+3)	(5+3)
0+4	1+4	2+4	3+4	4+4	(5+4)
0+5	1+5	2+5	3+5	4+5	5+5
0+6	1+6	2+6	3+6	4+6	5+6
0+7	1+7	2+7	3+7	4+7	5+7
0+8	1+8	2+8	3+8	4+8	5+8
0+9	1+9	2+9	3+9	4+9	5+9
0+10	1+10	2+10	3+10	4+10	5+10
0+11	1+11	2+11	3+11	4+11	5+11
0+12	1+12	2+12	3+12	4+12	5+12
0+13	1+13	2+13	3+13	4+13	5+13
0+14	1+14	2+14	3+14	4+14	5+14
0+15	1+15	2+15	3+15	4+15	5+15
0+16	1+16	2+16	3+16	4+16	
0+17	1+17	2+17	3+17		
0+18	1+18	2+18			
0+19	1+19				
0+20					

(6+0)	(7+0)	(8+0)	(9+0)	(10+0)	(11+0)
(6+1)	(7+1)	(8+1)	(9+1)	(10+1)	(11+1)
(7+2)	(7+2)	(8+2)	(9+2)	(10+2)	(11+2)
(6+3)	(7+3)	(8+3)	(9+3)	(10+3)	(11+3)
(6+4)	(7+4)	(8+4)	(9+4)	(10+4)	(11+4)
(6+5)	(7+5)	(8+5)	(9+5)	(10+5)	(11+5)
6+6	(7+6)	(8+6)	(9+6)	(10+6)	(11+6)
6+7	7+7	(8+7)	(9+7)	(10+7)	(11+7)
6+8	7+8	8+8	(9+8)	(10+8)	(11+8)
6+9	7+9	8+9	9+9	(10+9)	(11+9)
6+10	7+10	8+10	9+10	10+10	
6+11	7+11	8+11			
6+12	7+12	8+12			
6+13	7+13				
6+14					

(12+0)	(13+0)	(14+0)	(15+0)	(16+0)	(17+0)
(12+1)	(13+1)	(14+1)	(15+1)	(16+1)	(17+1)
(12+2)	(13+2)	(14+2)	(15+2)	(16+2)	(17+2)
(12+3)	(13+3)	(14+3)	(15+3)	(16+3)	(17+3)
(12+4)	(13+4)	(14+4)	(15+4)	(16+4)	
(12+5)	(13+5)	(14+5)	(15+5)		
(12+6)	(13+6)	(14+6)			
(12+7)	(13+7)				
(12+8)					

(18+0)	(19+0)	(20+0)
(18+1)	(19+1)	
(18+2)		

The Hierarchical Progression of Strategies

By grouping similar questions, this book will take you through a tried and tested system, teaching facts step-by-step in the following order

Strategy A	Add 1
Strategy B	Add 0
Strategy C	Add 10
Strategy D	Add 2
Strategy E	Add 11
Strategy F	Add 12
Strategy G	Add 9
Strategy H	Doubles
Strategy I	Near Doubles (Double +1) *i.e. 3+4, 5+6, 7+8 (and commutati*
Strategy J	Double (+1) +10 *i.e. 13+4, 14+5 (and commutative)*
Strategy K	Make 10
Strategy L	Make 20
Strategy M	Use 'Make 10' *i.e.* *(3+7=10 so 4+7=11), (2+8=10 so 4+8*

(3+7=10 so 5+7=12), (2+8=10 so 5+8

(6+4=10 so 6+8=14), (3+7=10 so 3+5

(3+7=10 so 3+6=9), (3+16=19)

(2+8=10 so 3+8=11)

Teachers' Notes - Addition Facts Diagnostic Test

The sheets are not intended to be used in the order laid out in the book. Sheets should be selected according to the ability of the child or to a specific learning objective that is being taught. The diagnostic test below can help to decide targets for individual children to work towards. The test clearly shows how the exercises develop and where they can be found in the book. The questions below should be read out and the children individually write down the answers.

1   It should be explained to the children that the easiest facts are at the top of each column and that the facts at the bottom of each column may be more difficult so they should not worry or linger over a fact if they cannot remember it.

2   Children should be told to put a line (e.g.—) if they are unsure of the answer, as this will help them progress to the next question rather than get behind.

3   The teacher should read the questions quite quickly as this test is to assess instant recall rather than testing whether children can 'work out' the addition facts.

Questions to be read aloud by teacher

① 1 + 17 =	⑪ 10 + 6 =	㉑ 4 + 10 =	㉛ 6 + 0 =
② 7 + 2 =	⑫ 8 + 2 =	㉒ 9 + 2 =	㉜ 14 + 2 =
③ 7 + 11 =	⑬ 11 + 4 =	㉓ 5 + 11 =	㉝ 8 + 11 =
④ 12 + 6 =	⑭ 3 + 12 =	㉔ 8 + 12 =	㉞ 4 + 12 =
⑤ 4 + 9 =	⑮ 9 + 3 =	㉕ 9 + 7 =	㉟ 8 + 9 =
⑥ 7 + 7 =	⑯ 8 + 8 =	㉖ 9 + 9 =	㊱ 6 + 6 =
⑦ 4 + 5 =	⑰ 7 + 8 =	㉗ 6 + 7 =	㊲ 3 + 4 =
⑧ 14 + 4 =	⑱ 13 + 4 =	㉘ 15 + 4 =	㊳ 13 + 3 =
⑨ 3 + 8 =	⑲ 15 + 3 =	㉙ 4 + 8 =	㊴ 5 + 3 =
⑩ 7 + 4 =	⑳ 6 + 3 =	㉚ 7 + 5 =	㊵ 6 + 8 =

Pupil's Answer Sheet

Children should write their answers in the spaces provided. Ticks and crosses should be used to mark the work. Four crosses in a line e.g. Qu 5, 15, 25 & 35 would show more work required on Strategy G: Add 9.

Addition Assessment Sheet (Recall of Facts)

Name _____   Date _____

				Strategy Tested	Exercises to go to if any facts incorrect
①	⑪	㉑	㉛	+1, 10, 0	1, 2, 3, 17, 26, 27, 35
②	⑫	㉒	㉜	+2	4, 14, 18, 28, 36
③	⑬	㉓	㉝	+11	5, 19, 29, 37
④	⑭	㉔	㉞	+12	6, 20, 30, 38
⑤	⑮	㉕	㉟	+9	7, 15, 21, 31, 39
⑥	⑯	㉖	㊱	Doubles	8, 22, 40
⑦	⑰	㉗	㊲	Double +1	9, 23, 32, 41
⑧	⑱	㉘	㊳	Double +1,+10	10, 16, 24, 33, 42
⑨	⑲	㉙	㊴	Use 'Make 10'	11, 12
⑩	⑳	㉚	㊵	Use 'Make 10'	then 13, 25, 34, 43

Exercise 1A	Exercise 1B	Exercise 1C	Exercise 1D
Name:	Name:	Name:	Name:
Date:	Date:	Date:	Date:

(1) $7 + 1 =$	(26) $1 + 2 =$	(51) $1 + 4 =$	(76) $1 + 5 =$
(2) $8 + 1 =$	(27) $9 + 1 =$	(52) $1 + 9 =$	(77) $1 + 1 =$
(3) $1 + 19 =$	(28) $1 + 11 =$	(53) $12 + 1 =$	(78) $7 + 1 =$
(4) $4 + 1 =$	(29) $1 + 15 =$	(54) $1 + 1 =$	(79) $1 + 9 =$
(5) $1 + 7 =$	(30) $1 + 7 =$	(55) $1 + 16 =$	(80) $1 + 11 =$
(6) $1 + 9 =$	(31) $3 + 1 =$	(56) $19 + 1 =$	(81) $15 + 1 =$
(7) $12 + 1 =$	(32) $14 + 1 =$	(57) $1 + 8 =$	(82) $17 + 1 =$
(8) $1 + 2 =$	(33) $1 + 7 =$	(58) $10 + 1 =$	(83) $1 + 13 =$
(9) $1 + 5 =$	(34) $17 + 1 =$	(59) $1 + 11 =$	(84) $1 + 19 =$
(10) $14 + 1 =$	(35) $1 + 6 =$	(60) $18 + 1 =$	(85) $5 + 1 =$
(11) $1 + 19 =$	(36) $7 + 1 =$	(61) $1 + 9 =$	(86) $1 + 3 =$
(12) $16 + 1 =$	(37) $12 + 1 =$	(62) $1 + 2 =$	(87) $2 + 1 =$
(13) $1 + 18 =$	(38) $1 + 19 =$	(63) $1 + 15 =$	(88) $1 + 18 =$
(14) $1 + 1 =$	(39) $1 + 16 =$	(64) $6 + 1 =$	(89) $9 + 1 =$
(15) $10 + 1 =$	(40) $8 + 1 =$	(65) $17 + 1 =$	(90) $1 + 4 =$
(16) $1 + 5 =$	(41) $13 + 1 =$	(66) $1 + 11 =$	(91) $10 + 1 =$
(17) $18 + 1 =$	(42) $1 + 4 =$	(67) $4 + 1 =$	(92) $1 + 3 =$
(18) $1 + 13 =$	(43) $1 + 9 =$	(68) $1 + 8 =$	(93) $19 + 1 =$
(19) $1 + 11 =$	(44) $18 + 1 =$	(69) $1 + 3 =$	(94) $1 + 16 =$
(20) $8 + 1 =$	(45) $1 + 12 =$	(70) $10 + 1 =$	(95) $1 + 10 =$
(21) $1 + 17 =$	(46) $18 + 1 =$	(71) $1 + 7 =$	(96) $4 + 1 =$
(22) $3 + 1 =$	(47) $1 + 1 =$	(72) $14 + 1 =$	(97) $1 + 8 =$
(23) $15 + 1 =$	(48) $8 + 1 =$	(73) $1 + 5 =$	(98) $12 + 1 =$
(24) $6 + 1 =$	(49) $10 + 1 =$	(74) $13 + 1 =$	(99) $14 + 1 =$
(25) $1 + 8 =$	(50) $1 + 5 =$	(75) $1 + 14 =$	(100) $1 + 6 =$

Time?	Time?	Time?	Time?
How did you do?	Have you reached your target?	Try to be faster?	What is your time?

Exercise 2A	Exercise 2B	Exercise 2C	Exercise 2D
Name:	Name:	Name:	Name:
Date:	Date:	Date:	Date:

1 $7 + 0 =$	**26** $0 + 12 =$	**51** $0 + 3 =$	**76** $0 + 5 =$
2 $0 + 18 =$	**27** $9 + 0 =$	**52** $10 + 0 =$	**77** $9 + 0 =$
3 $2 + 0 =$	**28** $0 + 19 =$	**53** $0 + 7 =$	**78** $0 + 13 =$
4 $0 + 12 =$	**29** $0 + 5 =$	**54** $0 + 1 =$	**79** $17 + 0 =$
5 $15 + 0 =$	**30** $17 + 0 =$	**55** $12 + 0 =$	**80** $0 + 11 =$
6 $9 + 0 =$	**31** $0 + 7 =$	**56** $0 + 17 =$	**81** $0 + 7 =$
7 $0 + 14 =$	**32** $3 + 0 =$	**57** $4 + 0 =$	**82** $6 + 0 =$
8 $18 + 0 =$	**33** $11 + 0 =$	**58** $8 + 0 =$	**83** $0 + 1 =$
9 $0 + 3 =$	**34** $0 + 13 =$	**59** $0 + 2 =$	**84** $0 + 15 =$
10 $0 + 6 =$	**35** $18 + 0 =$	**60** $0 + 14 =$	**85** $20 + 0 =$
11 $10 + 0 =$	**36** $0 + 10 =$	**61** $6 + 0 =$	**86** $8 + 0 =$
12 $6 + 0 =$	**37** $15 + 0 =$	**62** $5 + 0 =$	**87** $0 + 3 =$
13 $0 + 1 =$	**38** $6 + 0 =$	**63** $0 + 7 =$	**88** $0 + 18 =$
14 $19 + 0 =$	**39** $0 + 8 =$	**64** $0 + 9 =$	**89** $12 + 0 =$
15 $0 + 8 =$	**40** $0 + 2 =$	**65** $16 + 0 =$	**90** $10 + 0 =$
16 $5 + 0 =$	**41** $1 + 0 =$	**66** $18 + 0 =$	**91** $0 + 10 =$
17 $0 + 17 =$	**42** $0 + 4 =$	**67** $0 + 2 =$	**92** $8 + 0 =$
18 $0 + 8 =$	**43** $15 + 0 =$	**68** $0 + 11 =$	**93** $0 + 7 =$
19 $4 + 0 =$	**44** $0 + 0 =$	**69** $19 + 0 =$	**94** $11 + 0 =$
20 $13 + 0 =$	**45** $0 + 16 =$	**70** $3 + 0 =$	**95** $16 + 0 =$
21 $0 + 11 =$	**46** $7 + 0 =$	**71** $0 + 15 =$	**96** $0 + 2 =$
22 $20 + 0 =$	**47** $0 + 6 =$	**72** $0 + 20 =$	**97** $0 + 14 =$
23 $0 + 5 =$	**48** $14 + 0 =$	**73** $4 + 0 =$	**98** $9 + 0 =$
24 $13 + 0 =$	**49** $0 + 20 =$	**74** $13 + 10 =$	**99** $19 + 0 =$
25 $0 + 16 =$	**50** $8 + 0 =$	**75** $0 + 6 =$	**100** $0 + 4 =$

Time?	Time?	Time?	Time?
Did you beat your score?	Is this your best score yet?	Try to be even quicker next time!	Did you use any strategies?

Exercise 3A	Exercise 3B	Exercise 3C	Exercise 3D
Name:	Name:	Name:	Name:
Date:	Date:	Date:	Date:

#	Exercise 3A	#	Exercise 3B	#	Exercise 3C	#	Exercise 3D
1	$4 + 10 =$	26	$10 + 2 =$	51	$10 + 3 =$	76	$10 + 7 =$
2	$10 + 7 =$	27	$6 + 10 =$	52	$9 + 10 =$	77	$5 + 10 =$
3	$1 + 10 =$	28	$10 + 4 =$	53	$10 + 5 =$	78	$8 + 10 =$
4	$10 + 2 =$	29	$9 + 10 =$	54	$7 + 10 =$	79	$10 + 9 =$
5	$8 + 10 =$	30	$10 + 1 =$	55	$10 + 3 =$	80	$4 + 10 =$
6	$3 + 10 =$	31	$10 + 6 =$	56	$2 + 10 =$	81	$6 + 10 =$
7	$10 + 5 =$	32	$8 + 10 =$	57	$8 + 10 =$	82	$8 + 10 =$
8	$2 + 10 =$	33	$3 + 10 =$	58	$10 + 1 =$	83	$10 + 1 =$
9	$7 + 10 =$	34	$10 + 7 =$	59	$10 + 4 =$	84	$4 + 10 =$
10	$10 + 0 =$	35	$0 + 10 =$	60	$5 + 10 =$	85	$10 + 2 =$
11	$4 + 10 =$	36	$10 + 5 =$	61	$10 + 0 =$	86	$4 + 10 =$
12	$10 + 6 =$	37	$9 + 10 =$	62	$8 + 10 =$	87	$10 + 0 =$
13	$8 + 10 =$	38	$2 + 10 =$	63	$10 + 2 =$	88	$2 + 10 =$
14	$10 + 2 =$	39	$10 + 1 =$	64	$3 + 10 =$	89	$6 + 10 =$
15	$10 + 9 =$	40	$8 + 10 =$	65	$10 + 6 =$	90	$10 + 3 =$
16	$7 + 10 =$	41	$10 + 0 =$	66	$10 + 0 =$	91	$5 + 10 =$
17	$5 + 10 =$	42	$8 + 10 =$	67	$6 + 10 =$	92	$10 + 3 =$
18	$10 + 4 =$	43	$10 + 2 =$	68	$1 + 10 =$	93	$10 + 0 =$
19	$0 + 10 =$	44	$4 + 10 =$	69	$10 + 9 =$	94	$9 + 10 =$
20	$10 + 5 =$	45	$5 + 10 =$	70	$4 + 10 =$	95	$7 + 10 =$
21	$10 + 6 =$	46	$10 + 7 =$	71	$10 + 7 =$	96	$10 + 5 =$
22	$7 + 10 =$	47	$4 + 10 =$	72	$3 + 10 =$	97	$3 + 10 =$
23	$10 + 3 =$	48	$10 + 5 =$	73	$10 + 5 =$	98	$10 + 6 =$
24	$6 + 10 =$	49	$10 + 9 =$	74	$10 + 0 =$	99	$1 + 10 =$
25	$9 + 10 =$	50	$3 + 10 =$	75	$6 + 10 =$	100	$2 + 10 =$

Time?	Time?	Time?	Time?

Which facts did you find the hardest?

Did you beat your target?

Can you try to be faster?

Where do you need to improve?

Exercise 4A	Exercise 4B	Exercise 4C	Exercise 4D
Name:	Name:	Name:	Name:
Date:	Date:	Date:	Date:

1 $4 + 2 =$	26 $2 + 3 =$	51 $2 + 4 =$	76 $2 + 9 =$
2 $2 + 8 =$	27 $10 + 2 =$	52 $4 + 2 =$	77 $2 + 5 =$
3 $2 + 9 =$	28 $4 + 2 =$	53 $2 + 2 =$	78 $15 + 2 =$
4 $2 + 2 =$	29 $2 + 13 =$	54 $2 + 7 =$	79 $10 + 2 =$
5 $5 + 2 =$	30 $2 + 8 =$	55 $14 + 2 =$	80 $2 + 16 =$
6 $2 + 12 =$	31 $15 + 2 =$	56 $2 + 12 =$	81 $2 + 2 =$
7 $10 + 2 =$	32 $2 + 16 =$	57 $2 + 18 =$	82 $2 + 14 =$
8 $2 + 18 =$	33 $13 + 2 =$	58 $16 + 2 =$	83 $10 + 2 =$
9 $2 + 6 =$	34 $12 + 2 =$	59 $12 + 2 =$	84 $2 + 9 =$
10 $14 + 2 =$	35 $2 + 2 =$	60 $2 + 5 =$	85 $2 + 11 =$
11 $12 + 2 =$	36 $2 + 9 =$	61 $2 + 1 =$	86 $6 + 2 =$
12 $2 + 1 =$	37 $5 + 2 =$	62 $9 + 2 =$	87 $14 + 2 =$
13 $2 + 16 =$	38 $2 + 18 =$	63 $13 + 2 =$	88 $2 + 16 =$
14 $9 + 2 =$	39 $11 + 2 =$	64 $2 + 11 =$	89 $13 + 2 =$
15 $2 + 1 =$	40 $14 + 2 =$	65 $2 + 8 =$	90 $1 + 2 =$
16 $4 + 2 =$	41 $2 + 6 =$	66 $17 + 2 =$	91 $2 + 18 =$
17 $2 + 7 =$	42 $16 + 2 =$	67 $2 + 9 =$	92 $2 + 7 =$
18 $13 + 2 =$	43 $10 + 2 =$	68 $11 + 2 =$	93 $13 + 2 =$
19 $2 + 11 =$	44 $2 + 12 =$	69 $2 + 13 =$	94 $2 + 11 =$
20 $17 + 2 =$	45 $2 + 14 =$	70 $2 + 15 =$	95 $12 + 2 =$
21 $13 + 2 =$	46 $17 + 2 =$	71 $7 + 2 =$	96 $2 + 15 =$
22 $2 + 2 =$	47 $2 + 15 =$	72 $2 + 3 =$	97 $8 + 2 =$
23 $2 + 8 =$	48 $7 + 2 =$	73 $6 + 2 =$	98 $2 + 3 =$
24 $15 + 2 =$	49 $2 + 1 =$	74 $2 + 10 =$	99 $12 + 2 =$
25 $2 + 3 =$	50 $11 + 2 =$	75 $9 + 2 =$	100 $2 + 17 =$

Time?	Time?	Time?	Time?

Is this your best score?   Have you reached your target?   Did you do well?   Do you think you are improving?

Exercise 5A	Exercise 5B	Exercise 5C	Exercise 5D
Name:	Name:	Name:	Name:
Date:	Date:	Date:	Date:
1 $7 + 11 =$	26 $11 + 3 =$	51 $11 + 2 =$	76 $2 + 11 =$
2 $11 + 6 =$	27 $6 + 11 =$	52 $9 + 11 =$	77 $11 + 1 =$
3 $2 + 11 =$	28 $11 + 7 =$	53 $11 + 5 =$	78 $6 + 11 =$
4 $6 + 11 =$	29 $1 + 11 =$	54 $3 + 11 =$	79 $3 + 11 =$
5 $11 + 1 =$	30 $11 + 8 =$	55 $2 + 11 =$	80 $11 + 5 =$
6 $5 + 11 =$	31 $11 + 2 =$	56 $11 + 5 =$	81 $11 + 9 =$
7 $11 + 4 =$	32 $2 + 11 =$	57 $6 + 11 =$	82 $5 + 11 =$
8 $11 + 2 =$	33 $5 + 11 =$	58 $4 + 11 =$	83 $11 + 7 =$
9 $9 + 11 =$	34 $11 + 8 =$	59 $11 + 1 =$	84 $2 + 11 =$
10 $11 + 4 =$	35 $6 + 11 =$	60 $8 + 11 =$	85 $11 + 3 =$
11 $8 + 11 =$	36 $11 + 3 =$	61 $11 + 7 =$	86 $11 + 5 =$
12 $11 + 1 =$	37 $11 + 9 =$	62 $11 + 2 =$	87 $6 + 11 =$
13 $11 + 4 =$	38 $6 + 11 =$	63 $6 + 11 =$	88 $1 + 11 =$
14 $3 + 11 =$	39 $9 + 11 =$	64 $3 + 11 =$	89 $11 + 8 =$
15 $11 + 8 =$	40 $11 + 4 =$	65 $11 + 5 =$	90 $7 + 11 =$
16 $7 + 11 =$	41 $7 + 11 =$	66 $9 + 11 =$	91 $11 + 4 =$
17 $11 + 3 =$	42 $11 + 5 =$	67 $7 + 11 =$	92 $3 + 11 =$
18 $6 + 11 =$	43 $4 + 11 =$	68 $11 + 6 =$	93 $4 + 11 =$
19 $5 + 11 =$	44 $7 + 11 =$	69 $11 + 9 =$	94 $11 + 9 =$
20 $11 + 7 =$	45 $11 + 1 =$	70 $1 + 11 =$	95 $6 + 11 =$
21 $11 + 5 =$	46 $11 + 9 =$	71 $4 + 11 =$	96 $11 + 8 =$
22 $9 + 11 =$	47 $8 + 11 =$	72 $11 + 8 =$	97 $11 + 9 =$
23 $11 + 8 =$	48 $11 + 4 =$	73 $8 + 11 =$	98 $4 + 11 =$
24 $6 + 11 =$	49 $3 + 11 =$	74 $11 + 7 =$	99 $2 + 11 =$
25 $11 + 3 =$	50 $11 + 5 =$	75 $4 + 11 =$	100 $11 + 7 =$
Time?	Time?	Time?	Time?

Try to concentrate even more!

How do you think you are doing?

What have you learnt today?

How could you recall these facts even quicker?

	Exercise 6A		Exercise 6B		Exercise 6C		Exercise 6D
	Name:		Name:		Name:		Name:
	Date:		Date:		Date:		Date:
1	7 + 12 =	26	12 + 2 =	51	12 + 4 =	76	8 + 12 =
2	12 + 4 =	27	8 + 12 =	52	8 + 12 =	77	12 + 3 =
3	2 + 12 =	28	12 + 7 =	53	12 + 2 =	78	7 + 12 =
4	12 + 2 =	29	6 + 12 =	54	7 + 12 =	79	5 + 12 =
5	12 + 7 =	30	12 + 1 =	55	3 + 12 =	80	12 + 8 =
6	5 + 12 =	31	12 + 5 =	56	12 + 2 =	81	1 + 12 =
7	7 + 12 =	32	2 + 12 =	57	12 + 6 =	82	4 + 12 =
8	12 + 6 =	33	12 + 3 =	58	8 + 12 =	83	12 + 7 =
9	1 + 12 =	34	8 + 12 =	59	7 + 12 =	84	4 + 12 =
10	12 + 3 =	35	12 + 6 =	60	12 + 1 =	85	12 + 8 =
11	3 + 12 =	36	4 + 12 =	61	6 + 12 =	86	12 + 5 =
12	4 + 12 =	37	12 + 1 =	62	12 + 3 =	87	3 + 12 =
13	12 + 8 =	38	4 + 12 =	63	7 + 12 =	88	12 + 2 =
14	12 + 1 =	39	8 + 12 =	64	6 + 12 =	89	8 + 12 =
15	8 + 12 =	40	12 + 4 =	65	12 + 5 =	90	12 + 4 =
16	12 + 2 =	41	7 + 12 =	66	12 + 8 =	91	6 + 12 =
17	5 + 12 =	42	12 + 7 =	67	2 + 12 =	92	12 + 1 =
18	12 + 5 =	43	12 + 5 =	68	12 + 6 =	93	4 + 12 =
19	6 + 12 =	44	1 + 12 =	69	4 + 12 =	94	3 + 12 =
20	12 + 4 =	45	6 + 12 =	70	7 + 12 =	95	12 + 5 =
21	7 + 12 =	46	12 + 3 =	71	12 + 1 =	96	6 + 12 =
22	4 + 12 =	47	8 + 12 =	72	5 + 12 =	97	12 + 7 =
23	12 + 1 =	48	3 + 12 =	73	4 + 12 =	98	1 + 12 =
24	12 + 6 =	49	12 + 8 =	74	12 + 3 =	99	6 + 12 =
25	3 + 12 =	50	12 + 5 =	75	8 + 12 =	100	12 + 2 =

Time? | Time? | Time? | Time?

Are the facts at your fingertips? | Try to really focus! | Which facts do you find the easiest? | Did you do well?

Exercise 7A	Exercise 7B	Exercise 7C	Exercise 7D
Name:	Name:	Name:	Name:
Date:	Date:	Date:	Date:
1. $4 + 9 =$	26. $2 + 9 =$	51. $9 + 5 =$	76. $9 + 4 =$
2. $7 + 9 =$	27. $9 + 7 =$	52. $3 + 9 =$	77. $6 + 9 =$
3. $9 + 6 =$	28. $5 + 9 =$	53. $9 + 6 =$	78. $9 + 8 =$
4. $1 + 9 =$	29. $9 + 8 =$	54. $5 + 9 =$	79. $3 + 9 =$
5. $9 + 4 =$	30. $5 + 9 =$	55. $9 + 11 =$	80. $9 + 6 =$
6. $10 + 9 =$	31. $6 + 9 =$	56. $9 + 9 =$	81. $8 + 9 =$
7. $8 + 9 =$	32. $9 + 11 =$	57. $4 + 9 =$	82. $3 + 9 =$
8. $9 + 9 =$	33. $7 + 9 =$	58. $9 + 3 =$	83. $9 + 11 =$
9. $5 + 9 =$	34. $9 + 6 =$	59. $9 + 7 =$	84. $9 + 1 =$
10. $9 + 3 =$	35. $9 + 7 =$	60. $4 + 9 =$	85. $2 + 9 =$
11. $11 + 9 =$	36. $10 + 9 =$	61. $9 + 6 =$	86. $5 + 9 =$
12. $8 + 9 =$	37. $4 + 9 =$	62. $8 + 9 =$	87. $9 + 6 =$
13. $9 + 6 =$	38. $9 + 3 =$	63. $9 + 9 =$	88. $8 + 9 =$
14. $9 + 9 =$	39. $6 + 9 =$	64. $1 + 9 =$	89. $9 + 7 =$
15. $4 + 9 =$	40. $9 + 8 =$	65. $6 + 9 =$	90. $8 + 9 =$
16. $9 + 3 =$	41. $9 + 1 =$	66. $9 + 11 =$	91. $9 + 5 =$
17. $2 + 9 =$	42. $11 + 9 =$	67. $9 + 8 =$	92. $7 + 9 =$
18. $8 + 9 =$	43. $8 + 9 =$	68. $11 + 9 =$	93. $9 + 9 =$
19. $9 + 11 =$	44. $9 + 10 =$	69. $9 + 7 =$	94. $9 + 2 =$
20. $7 + 9 =$	45. $9 + 8 =$	70. $2 + 9 =$	95. $6 + 9 =$
21. $5 + 9 =$	46. $9 + 1 =$	71. $9 + 10 =$	96. $4 + 9 =$
22. $9 + 2 =$	47. $9 + 9 =$	72. $7 + 9 =$	97. $9 + 7 =$
23. $9 + 6 =$	48. $3 + 9 =$	73. $10 + 9 =$	98. $9 + 10 =$
24. $10 + 9 =$	49. $9 + 2 =$	74. $9 + 7 =$	99. $5 + 9 =$
25. $9 + 7 =$	50. $4 + 9 =$	75. $2 + 9 =$	100. $9 + 3 =$
Time?	Time?	Time?	Time?

Did you beat your score?

Which facts do you find the hardest?

Is this your best score?

Try to concentrate even more?

Exercise 8A	Exercise 8B	Exercise 8C	Exercise 8D
Name:	Name:	Name:	Name:
Date:	Date:	Date:	Date:

1 $7 + 7 =$	**26** $4 + 4 =$	**51** $2 + 2 =$	**76** $7 + 7 =$
2 $4 + 4 =$	**27** $3 + 3 =$	**52** $4 + 4 =$	**77** $3 + 3 =$
3 $9 + 9 =$	**28** $10 + 10 =$	**53** $5 + 5 =$	**78** $1 + 1 =$
4 $3 + 3 =$	**29** $6 + 6 =$	**54** $3 + 3 =$	**79** $8 + 8 =$
5 $1 + 1 =$	**30** $8 + 8 =$	**55** $7 + 7 =$	**80** $3 + 3 =$
6 $4 + 4 =$	**31** $5 + 5 =$	**56** $9 + 9 =$	**81** $7 + 7 =$
7 $3 + 3 =$	**32** $10 + 10 =$	**57** $7 + 7 =$	**82** $10 + 10 =$
8 $8 + 8 =$	**33** $9 + 9 =$	**58** $4 + 4 =$	**83** $2 + 2 =$
9 $7 + 7 =$	**34** $4 + 4 =$	**59** $3 + 3 =$	**84** $9 + 9 =$
10 $5 + 5 =$	**35** $6 + 6 =$	**60** $1 + 1 =$	**85** $8 + 8 =$
11 $2 + 2 =$	**36** $2 + 2 =$	**61** $7 + 7 =$	**86** $6 + 6 =$
12 $10 + 10 =$	**37** $1 + 1 =$	**62** $5 + 5 =$	**87** $2 + 2 =$
13 $4 + 4 =$	**38** $3 + 3 =$	**63** $8 + 8 =$	**88** $10 + 10 =$
14 $5 + 5 =$	**39** $9 + 9 =$	**64** $10 + 10 =$	**89** $1 + 1 =$
15 $1 + 1 =$	**40** $3 + 3 =$	**65** $9 + 9 =$	**90** $6 + 6 =$
16 $6 + 6 =$	**41** $4 + 4 =$	**66** $1 + 1 =$	**91** $4 + 4 =$
17 $8 + 8 =$	**42** $8 + 8 =$	**67** $8 + 8 =$	**92** $3 + 3 =$
18 $6 + 6 =$	**43** $7 + 7 =$	**68** $6 + 6 =$	**93** $2 + 2 =$
19 $10 + 10 =$	**44** $1 + 1 =$	**69** $2 + 2 =$	**94** $6 + 6 =$
20 $7 + 7 =$	**45** $5 + 5 =$	**70** $9 + 9 =$	**95** $4 + 4 =$
21 $6 + 6 =$	**46** $8 + 8 =$	**71** $2 + 2 =$	**96** $8 + 8 =$
22 $5 + 5 =$	**47** $1 + 1 =$	**72** $10 + 10 =$	**97** $5 + 5 =$
23 $2 + 2 =$	**48** $2 + 2 =$	**73** $3 + 3 =$	**98** $1 + 1 =$
24 $9 + 9 =$	**49** $7 + 7 =$	**74** $6 + 6 =$	**99** $9 + 9 =$
25 $7 + 7 =$	**50** $2 + 2 =$	**75** $8 + 8 =$	**100** $5 + 5 =$

Time?	Time?	Time?	Time?
Is this your best score yet?	Did you beat your target?	Have you reached your target yet?	How do you think you are doing?

Exercise 9A	Exercise 9B	Exercise 9C	Exercise 9D
Name:	Name:	Name:	Name:
Date:	Date:	Date:	Date:

1	$7 + 8 =$	**26**	$3 + 4 =$	**51**	$4 + 5 =$	**76**	$6 + 7 =$
2	$4 + 5 =$	**27**	$7 + 6 =$	**52**	$7 + 8 =$	**77**	$8 + 9 =$
3	$6 + 5 =$	**28**	$5 + 6 =$	**53**	$3 + 2 =$	**78**	$4 + 5 =$
4	$3 + 4 =$	**29**	$8 + 9 =$	**54**	$1 + 2 =$	**79**	$3 + 4 =$
5	$8 + 7 =$	**30**	$3 + 2 =$	**55**	$9 + 10 =$	**80**	$2 + 3 =$
6	$5 + 4 =$	**31**	$6 + 7 =$	**56**	$7 + 6 =$	**81**	$7 + 8 =$
7	$4 + 3 =$	**32**	$1 + 2 =$	**57**	$4 + 5 =$	**82**	$5 + 6 =$
8	$1 + 2 =$	**33**	$10 + 9 =$	**58**	$6 + 7 =$	**83**	$3 + 4 =$
9	$6 + 7 =$	**34**	$4 + 5 =$	**59**	$3 + 4 =$	**84**	$5 + 6 =$
10	$8 + 7 =$	**35**	$1 + 2 =$	**60**	$5 + 4 =$	**85**	$9 + 8 =$
11	$6 + 5 =$	**36**	$4 + 3 =$	**61**	$2 + 3 =$	**86**	$6 + 7 =$
12	$9 + 8 =$	**37**	$8 + 9 =$	**62**	$10 + 9 =$	**87**	$1 + 2 =$
13	$4 + 3 =$	**38**	$6 + 5 =$	**63**	$5 + 4 =$	**88**	$7 + 6 =$
14	$2 + 3 =$	**39**	$2 + 3 =$	**64**	$2 + 1 =$	**89**	$8 + 9 =$
15	$5 + 6 =$	**40**	$7 + 6 =$	**65**	$8 + 7 =$	**90**	$5 + 4 =$
16	$2 + 1 =$	**41**	$4 + 5 =$	**66**	$9 + 8 =$	**91**	$3 + 4 =$
17	$8 + 9 =$	**42**	$2 + 3 =$	**67**	$8 + 9 =$	**92**	$3 + 2 =$
18	$7 + 6 =$	**43**	$7 + 8 =$	**68**	$6 + 7 =$	**93**	$6 + 5 =$
19	$5 + 4 =$	**44**	$9 + 8 =$	**69**	$8 + 9 =$	**94**	$8 + 7 =$
20	$3 + 2 =$	**45**	$6 + 7 =$	**70**	$5 + 6 =$	**95**	$4 + 3 =$
21	$8 + 7 =$	**46**	$5 + 4 =$	**71**	$2 + 3 =$	**96**	$7 + 8 =$
22	$9 + 8 =$	**47**	$3 + 2 =$	**72**	$7 + 6 =$	**97**	$6 + 5 =$
23	$4 + 5 =$	**48**	$9 + 10 =$	**73**	$3 + 2 =$	**98**	$9 + 10 =$
24	$7 + 8 =$	**49**	$8 + 7 =$	**74**	$9 + 8 =$	**99**	$2 + 1 =$
25	$3 + 2 =$	**50**	$5 + 4 =$	**75**	$4 + 3 =$	**100**	$5 + 6 =$

Time?	Time?	Time?	Time?

Try to be even quicker next time!

Can you try to be faster?

Did you do well?

What have you learnt today?

Exercise 10A	Exercise 10B	Exercise 10C	Exercise 10D
Name:	Name:	Name:	Name:
Date:	Date:	Date:	Date:

1 $13 + 3 =$	**26** $11 + 1 =$	**51** $4 + 15 =$	**76** $5 + 15 =$
2 $15 + 4 =$	**27** $5 + 15 =$	**52** $2 + 12 =$	**77** $3 + 12 =$
3 $13 + 2 =$	**28** $2 + 13 =$	**53** $5 + 15 =$	**78** $4 + 15 =$
4 $5 + 15 =$	**29** $13 + 3 =$	**54** $11 + 2 =$	**79** $12 + 3 =$
5 $14 + 4 =$	**30** $12 + 1 =$	**55** $3 + 14 =$	**80** $2 + 11 =$
6 $2 + 12 =$	**31** $14 + 4 =$	**56** $14 + 5 =$	**81** $12 + 2 =$
7 $11 + 1 =$	**32** $2 + 13 =$	**57** $12 + 1 =$	**82** $1 + 11 =$
8 $14 + 5 =$	**33** $15 + 5 =$	**58** $1 + 11 =$	**83** $5 + 15 =$
9 $12 + 2 =$	**34** $3 + 14 =$	**59** $3 + 12 =$	**84** $11 + 2 =$
10 $3 + 13 =$	**35** $14 + 5 =$	**60** $5 + 15 =$	**85** $13 + 4 =$
11 $14 + 4 =$	**36** $12 + 2 =$	**61** $12 + 2 =$	**86** $2 + 13 =$
12 $1 + 11 =$	**37** $3 + 12 =$	**62** $4 + 14 =$	**87** $1 + 11 =$
13 $5 + 15 =$	**38** $14 + 4 =$	**63** $13 + 2 =$	**88** $12 + 1 =$
14 $12 + 3 =$	**39** $13 + 2 =$	**64** $11 + 1 =$	**89** $14 + 5 =$
15 $4 + 13 =$	**40** $5 + 15 =$	**65** $15 + 5 =$	**90** $3 + 13 =$
16 $14 + 5 =$	**41** $1 + 11 =$	**66** $12 + 3 =$	**91** $5 + 15 =$
17 $2 + 12 =$	**42** $13 + 4 =$	**67** $5 + 15 =$	**92** $3 + 12 =$
18 $5 + 15 =$	**43** $5 + 14 =$	**68** $13 + 2 =$	**93** $2 + 11 =$
19 $13 + 3 =$	**44** $4 + 14 =$	**69** $11 + 2 =$	**94** $13 + 3 =$
20 $12 + 1 =$	**45** $3 + 14 =$	**70** $2 + 12 =$	**95** $4 + 14 =$
21 $4 + 15 =$	**46** $15 + 5 =$	**71** $4 + 13 =$	**96** $5 + 14 =$
22 $4 + 14 =$	**47** $13 + 2 =$	**72** $13 + 3 =$	**97** $13 + 4 =$
23 $11 + 1 =$	**48** $11 + 2 =$	**73** $4 + 13 =$	**98** $5 + 15 =$
24 $13 + 4 =$	**49** $3 + 13 =$	**74** $14 + 4 =$	**99** $13 + 2 =$
25 $5 + 14 =$	**50** $12 + 3 =$	**75** $11 + 1 =$	**100** $2 + 12 =$

Time?	Time?	Time?	Time?
Did you use strategies?	Where can you improve?	Are you improving?	Did you do well?

Exercise 11A	Exercise 11B	Exercise 11C	Exercise 11D
Name:	Name:	Name:	Name:
Date:	Date:	Date:	Date:

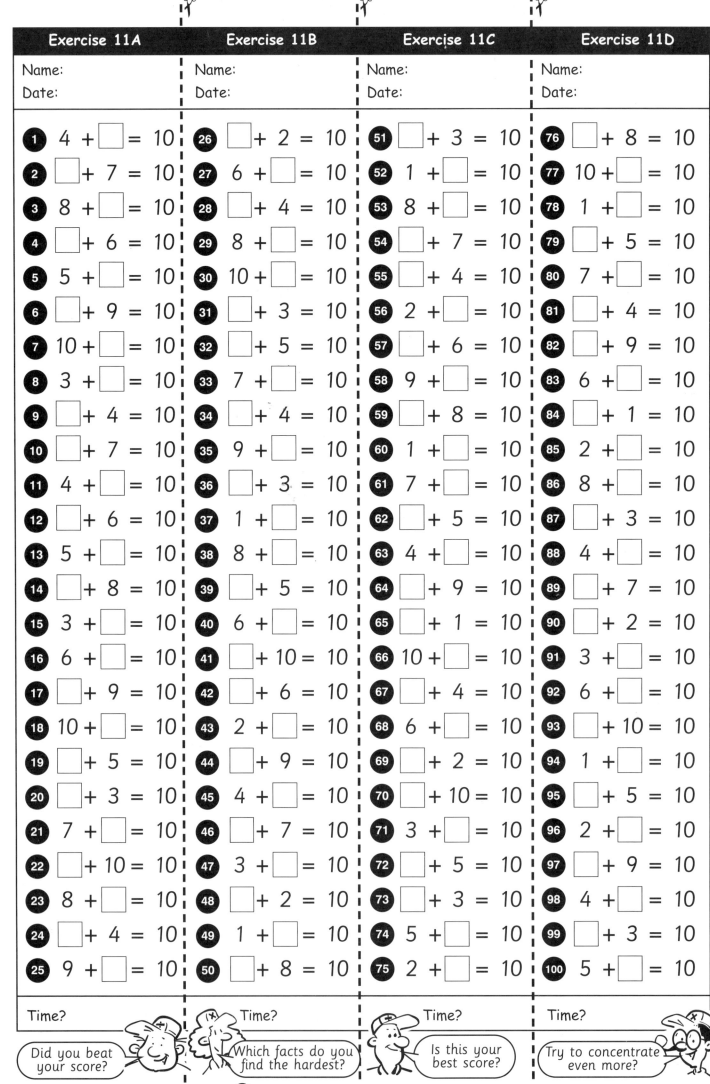

1 $4 + \square = 10$	**26** $\square + 2 = 10$	**51** $\square + 3 = 10$	**76** $\square + 8 = 10$
2 $\square + 7 = 10$	**27** $6 + \square = 10$	**52** $1 + \square = 10$	**77** $10 + \square = 10$
3 $8 + \square = 10$	**28** $\square + 4 = 10$	**53** $8 + \square = 10$	**78** $1 + \square = 10$
4 $\square + 6 = 10$	**29** $8 + \square = 10$	**54** $\square + 7 = 10$	**79** $\square + 5 = 10$
5 $5 + \square = 10$	**30** $10 + \square = 10$	**55** $\square + 4 = 10$	**80** $7 + \square = 10$
6 $\square + 9 = 10$	**31** $\square + 3 = 10$	**56** $2 + \square = 10$	**81** $\square + 4 = 10$
7 $10 + \square = 10$	**32** $\square + 5 = 10$	**57** $\square + 6 = 10$	**82** $\square + 9 = 10$
8 $3 + \square = 10$	**33** $7 + \square = 10$	**58** $9 + \square = 10$	**83** $6 + \square = 10$
9 $\square + 4 = 10$	**34** $\square + 4 = 10$	**59** $\square + 8 = 10$	**84** $\square + 1 = 10$
10 $\square + 7 = 10$	**35** $9 + \square = 10$	**60** $1 + \square = 10$	**85** $2 + \square = 10$
11 $4 + \square = 10$	**36** $\square + 3 = 10$	**61** $7 + \square = 10$	**86** $8 + \square = 10$
12 $\square + 6 = 10$	**37** $1 + \square = 10$	**62** $\square + 5 = 10$	**87** $\square + 3 = 10$
13 $5 + \square = 10$	**38** $8 + \square = 10$	**63** $4 + \square = 10$	**88** $4 + \square = 10$
14 $\square + 8 = 10$	**39** $\square + 5 = 10$	**64** $\square + 9 = 10$	**89** $\square + 7 = 10$
15 $3 + \square = 10$	**40** $6 + \square = 10$	**65** $\square + 1 = 10$	**90** $\square + 2 = 10$
16 $6 + \square = 10$	**41** $\square + 10 = 10$	**66** $10 + \square = 10$	**91** $3 + \square = 10$
17 $\square + 9 = 10$	**42** $\square + 6 = 10$	**67** $\square + 4 = 10$	**92** $6 + \square = 10$
18 $10 + \square = 10$	**43** $2 + \square = 10$	**68** $6 + \square = 10$	**93** $\square + 10 = 10$
19 $\square + 5 = 10$	**44** $\square + 9 = 10$	**69** $\square + 2 = 10$	**94** $1 + \square = 10$
20 $\square + 3 = 10$	**45** $4 + \square = 10$	**70** $\square + 10 = 10$	**95** $\square + 5 = 10$
21 $7 + \square = 10$	**46** $\square + 7 = 10$	**71** $3 + \square = 10$	**96** $2 + \square = 10$
22 $\square + 10 = 10$	**47** $3 + \square = 10$	**72** $\square + 5 = 10$	**97** $\square + 9 = 10$
23 $8 + \square = 10$	**48** $\square + 2 = 10$	**73** $\square + 3 = 10$	**98** $4 + \square = 10$
24 $\square + 4 = 10$	**49** $1 + \square = 10$	**74** $5 + \square = 10$	**99** $\square + 3 = 10$
25 $9 + \square = 10$	**50** $\square + 8 = 10$	**75** $2 + \square = 10$	**100** $5 + \square = 10$

Time?	Time?	Time?	Time?

Did you beat your score?

Which facts do you find the hardest?

Is this your best score?

Try to concentrate even more?

Exercise 12A	Exercise 12B	Exercise 12C	Exercise 12D

Name: Date: Name: Date: Name: Date: Name: Date:

1. ☐ + 14 = 20
2. 7 + ☐ = 20
3. ☐ + 16 = 20
4. 5 + ☐ = 20
5. ☐ + 2 = 20
6. 8 + ☐ = 20
7. 11 + ☐ = 20
8. ☐ + 15 = 20
9. 4 + ☐ = 20
10. ☐ + 20 = 20
11. 6 + ☐ = 20
12. ☐ + 14 = 20
13. 1 + ☐ = 20
14. ☐ + 17 = 20
15. ☐ + 13 = 20
16. 9 + ☐ = 20
17. 2 + ☐ = 20
18. ☐ + 13 = 20
19. 7 + ☐ = 20
20. ☐ + 18 = 20
21. 3 + ☐ = 20
22. ☐ + 19 = 20
23. 10 + ☐ = 20
24. ☐ + 12 = 20
25. 0 + ☐ = 20

26. ☐ + 13 = 20
27. 1 + ☐ = 20
28. ☐ + 19 = 20
29. 9 + ☐ = 20
30. 8 + ☐ = 20
31. ☐ + 17 = 20
32. ☐ + 20 = 20
33. 2 + ☐ = 20
34. ☐ + 14 = 20
35. 7 + ☐ = 20
36. ☐ + 19 = 20
37. 3 + ☐ = 20
38. ☐ + 16 = 20
39. ☐ + 18 = 20
40. 10 + ☐ = 20
41. ☐ + 15 = 20
42. 12 + ☐ = 20
43. ☐ + 15 = 20
44. 4 + ☐ = 20
45. 11 + ☐ = 20
46. ☐ + 16 = 20
47. 5 + ☐ = 20
48. ☐ + 18 = 20
49. ☐ + 17 = 20
50. 6 + ☐ = 20

51. ☐ + 11 = 20
52. 8 + ☐ = 20
53. 5 + ☐ = 20
54. ☐ + 0 = 20
55. 7 + ☐ = 20
56. ☐ + 1 = 20
57. 12 + ☐ = 20
58. ☐ + 3 = 20
59. 4 + ☐ = 20
60. ☐ + 20 = 20
61. ☐ + 13 = 20
62. 10 + ☐ = 20
63. 14 + ☐ = 20
64. ☐ + 19 = 20
65. 1 + ☐ = 20
66. ☐ + 2 = 20
67. 6 + ☐ = 20
68. ☐ + 17 = 20
69. ☐ + 4 = 20
70. 2 + ☐ = 20
71. ☐ + 15 = 20
72. ☐ + 18 = 20
73. 3 + ☐ = 20
74. ☐ + 16 = 20
75. 9 + ☐ = 20

76. ☐ + 18 = 20
77. 4 + ☐ = 20
78. ☐ + 10 = 20
79. 20 + ☐ = 20
80. ☐ + 11 = 20
81. 5 + ☐ = 20
82. ☐ + 17 = 20
83. 1 + ☐ = 20
84. 6 + ☐ = 20
85. ☐ + 16 = 20
86. ☐ + 12 = 20
87. 2 + ☐ = 20
88. ☐ + 15 = 20
89. 19 + ☐ = 20
90. ☐ + 15 = 20
91. 17 + ☐ = 20
92. 8 + ☐ = 20
93. ☐ + 14 = 20
94. 9 + ☐ = 20
95. ☐ + 16 = 20
96. 3 + ☐ = 20
97. 18 + ☐ = 20
98. ☐ + 13 = 20
99. 7 + ☐ = 20
100. ☐ + 9 = 20

Exercise 12 — Missing Box — What Makes 20

Time? Is this your best score yet? Did you beat your target? Have you reached your target yet? How do you think you are doing?

© **Topical Resources.** May be photocopied for classroom use only.

Exercise 13A	Exercise 13B	Exercise 13C	Exercise 13D
Name:	Name:	Name:	Name:
Date:	Date:	Date:	Date:

Exercise 13A	Exercise 13B	Exercise 13C	Exercise 13D
1 $7 + 4 =$	26 $3 + 5 =$	51 $3 + 5 =$	76 $3 + 6 =$
2 $3 + 8 =$	27 $4 + 7 =$	52 $6 + 8 =$	77 $4 + 8 =$
3 $5 + 7 =$	28 $8 + 5 =$	53 $3 + 5 =$	78 $5 + 7 =$
4 $6 + 3 =$	29 $13 + 5 =$	54 $5 + 8 =$	79 $5 + 3 =$
5 $8 + 4 =$	30 $3 + 6 =$	55 $3 + 5 =$	80 $3 + 5 =$
6 $4 + 7 =$	31 $4 + 8 =$	56 $4 + 7 =$	81 $5 + 8 =$
7 $3 + 5 =$	32 $6 + 3 =$	57 $5 + 8 =$	82 $8 + 4 =$
8 $6 + 8 =$	33 $7 + 5 =$	58 $4 + 8 =$	83 $8 + 5 =$
9 $4 + 7 =$	34 $3 + 8 =$	59 $3 + 5 =$	84 $3 + 5 =$
10 $8 + 5 =$	35 $5 + 7 =$	60 $5 + 7 =$	85 $4 + 7 =$
11 $3 + 8 =$	36 $8 + 6 =$	61 $3 + 5 =$	86 $5 + 8 =$
12 $5 + 3 =$	37 $4 + 7 =$	62 $8 + 4 =$	87 $7 + 5 =$
13 $8 + 4 =$	38 $3 + 5 =$	63 $6 + 8 =$	88 $3 + 5 =$
14 $3 + 5 =$	39 $5 + 3 =$	64 $3 + 6 =$	89 $8 + 5 =$
15 $8 + 6 =$	40 $3 + 6 =$	65 $5 + 8 =$	90 $6 + 8 =$
16 $8 + 5 =$	41 $8 + 4 =$	66 $8 + 6 =$	91 $3 + 6 =$
17 $3 + 8 =$	42 $3 + 6 =$	67 $7 + 5 =$	92 $7 + 4 =$
18 $5 + 7 =$	43 $5 + 8 =$	68 $3 + 15 =$	93 $5 + 8 =$
19 $4 + 8 =$	44 $8 + 6 =$	69 $3 + 5 =$	94 $3 + 5 =$
20 $3 + 6 =$	45 $8 + 3 =$	70 $8 + 5 =$	95 $8 + 6 =$
21 $5 + 3 =$	46 $3 + 5 =$	71 $7 + 4 =$	96 $5 + 7 =$
22 $8 + 5 =$	47 $8 + 5 =$	72 $3 + 8 =$	97 $3 + 8 =$
23 $3 + 5 =$	48 $6 + 8 =$	73 $5 + 7 =$	98 $3 + 5 =$
24 $3 + 5 =$	49 $3 + 5 =$	74 $3 + 6 =$	99 $6 + 8 =$
25 $5 + 8 =$	50 $4 + 8 =$	75 $7 + 5 =$	100 $3 + 5 =$

Time?	Time?	Time?	Time?

How did you do?

Did you beat your best score?

Can you try to be faster?

Have you reached your target?

Exercise 14A	Exercise 14B	Exercise 14C	Exercise 14D
Name:	Name:	Name:	Name:
Date:	Date:	Date:	Date:

1. $2 + 7 =$
2. $1 + 10 =$
3. $2 + 1 =$
4. $2 + 10 =$
5. $9 + 10 =$
6. $2 + 2 =$
7. $3 + 10 =$
8. $2 + 9 =$
9. $8 + 10 =$
10. $2 + 3 =$
11. $10 + 10 =$
12. $2 + 8 =$
13. $5 + 2 =$
14. $10 + 2 =$
15. $7 + 10 =$
16. $2 + 4 =$
17. $7 + 2 =$
18. $10 + 4 =$
19. $8 + 2 =$
20. $10 + 3 =$
21. $5 + 2 =$
22. $10 + 5 =$
23. $9 + 2 =$
24. $2 + 6 =$
25. $6 + 10 =$

26. $4 + 2 =$
27. $10 + 3 =$
28. $5 + 2 =$
29. $10 + 8 =$
30. $2 + 11 =$
31. $7 + 10 =$
32. $2 + 10 =$
33. $2 + 2 =$
34. $10 + 4 =$
35. $6 + 2 =$
36. $10 + 5 =$
37. $1 + 2 =$
38. $10 + 10 =$
39. $12 + 2 =$
40. $10 + 6 =$
41. $9 + 2 =$
42. $10 + 3 =$
43. $9 + 2 =$
44. $10 + 4 =$
45. $13 + 2 =$
46. $10 + 8 =$
47. $14 + 2 =$
48. $7 + 2 =$
49. $10 + 7 =$
50. $2 + 6 =$

51. $10 + 3 =$
52. $13 + 2 =$
53. $10 + 2 =$
54. $18 + 2 =$
55. $3 + 10 =$
56. $2 + 14 =$
57. $4 + 10 =$
58. $2 + 12 =$
59. $10 + 9 =$
60. $10 + 1 =$
61. $15 + 2 =$
62. $5 + 2 =$
63. $10 + 4 =$
64. $5 + 2 =$
65. $2 + 11 =$
66. $6 + 10 =$
67. $10 + 6 =$
68. $7 + 2 =$
69. $10 + 7 =$
70. $16 + 2 =$
71. $10 + 8 =$
72. $2 + 17 =$
73. $9 + 10 =$
74. $2 + 10 =$
75. $10 + 8 =$

76. $2 + 10 =$
77. $2 + 11 =$
78. $10 + 10 =$
79. $2 + 5 =$
80. $10 + 8 =$
81. $2 + 1 =$
82. $4 + 10 =$
83. $3 + 2 =$
84. $9 + 2 =$
85. $10 + 9 =$
86. $10 + 4 =$
87. $6 + 2 =$
88. $10 + 6 =$
89. $2 + 7 =$
90. $8 + 10 =$
91. $5 + 10 =$
92. $2 + 6 =$
93. $4 + 2 =$
94. $10 + 5 =$
95. $7 + 10 =$
96. $2 + 9 =$
97. $6 + 10 =$
98. $10 + 8 =$
99. $7 + 2 =$
100. $2 + 9 =$

Time? | Time? | Time? | Time?

How do you think you are doing? | How did you do? | Is this your best score? | Which facts do you find the easiest?

Exercise 15A	Exercise 15B	Exercise 15C	Exercise 15D
Name:	Name:	Name:	Name:
Date:	Date:	Date:	Date:

1	$3 + 9 =$	**26**	$12 + 5 =$	**51**	$11 + 6 =$	**76**	$12 + 3 =$
2	$11 + 7 =$	**27**	$4 + 9 =$	**52**	$7 + 9 =$	**77**	$4 + 9 =$
3	$2 + 12 =$	**28**	$11 + 4 =$	**53**	$12 + 5 =$	**78**	$12 + 6 =$
4	$6 + 11 =$	**29**	$5 + 12 =$	**54**	$11 + 8 =$	**79**	$3 + 9 =$
5	$9 + 6 =$	**30**	$9 + 3 =$	**55**	$6 + 9 =$	**80**	$1 + 12 =$
6	$5 + 12 =$	**31**	$6 + 11 =$	**56**	$12 + 7 =$	**81**	$5 + 9 =$
7	$11 + 4 =$	**32**	$12 + 6 =$	**57**	$9 + 5 =$	**82**	$12 + 2 =$
8	$7 + 9 =$	**33**	$11 + 2 =$	**58**	$8 + 9 =$	**83**	$2 + 12 =$
9	$12 + 8 =$	**34**	$9 + 7 =$	**59**	$11 + 4 =$	**84**	$9 + 11 =$
10	$11 + 8 =$	**35**	$7 + 12 =$	**60**	$4 + 12 =$	**85**	$11 + 4 =$
11	$9 + 9 =$	**36**	$9 + 11 =$	**61**	$12 + 3 =$	**86**	$6 + 12 =$
12	$12 + 3 =$	**37**	$8 + 11 =$	**62**	$9 + 9 =$	**87**	$9 + 10 =$
13	$11 + 2 =$	**38**	$12 + 8 =$	**63**	$10 + 9 =$	**88**	$7 + 9 =$
14	$9 + 2 =$	**39**	$10 + 9 =$	**64**	$12 + 3 =$	**89**	$12 + 4 =$
15	$10 + 9 =$	**40**	$12 + 8 =$	**65**	$11 + 9 =$	**90**	$8 + 11 =$
16	$12 + 5 =$	**41**	$3 + 9 =$	**66**	$5 + 12 =$	**91**	$9 + 9 =$
17	$9 + 11 =$	**42**	$11 + 9 =$	**67**	$9 + 4 =$	**92**	$11 + 9 =$
18	$11 + 9 =$	**43**	$2 + 9 =$	**68**	$6 + 12 =$	**93**	$12 + 7 =$
19	$9 + 9 =$	**44**	$9 + 10 =$	**69**	$2 + 11 =$	**94**	$6 + 12 =$
20	$12 + 7 =$	**45**	$3 + 12 =$	**70**	$2 + 9 =$	**95**	$9 + 5 =$
21	$4 + 11 =$	**46**	$12 + 6 =$	**71**	$11 + 9 =$	**96**	$11 + 7 =$
22	$9 + 6 =$	**47**	$4 + 11 =$	**72**	$10 + 9 =$	**97**	$5 + 12 =$
23	$5 + 12 =$	**48**	$9 + 11 =$	**73**	$12 + 7 =$	**98**	$9 + 6 =$
24	$1 + 11 =$	**49**	$5 + 12 =$	**74**	$9 + 2 =$	**99**	$9 + 9 =$
25	$10 + 9 =$	**50**	$9 + 7 =$	**75**	$1 + 12 =$	**100**	$12 + 8 =$

Time?	Time?	Time?	Time?

Did you do well?

What have you learnt today?

Have you reached your target?

What is your time?

Exercise 16A	Exercise 16B	Exercise 16C	Exercise 16D
Name:	Name:	Name:	Name:
Date:	Date:	Date:	Date:

1 $5 + 5 =$	**26** $8 + 7 =$	**51** $5 + 4 =$	**76** $10 + 10 =$
2 $14 + 3 =$	**27** $9 + 9 =$	**52** $3 + 12 =$	**77** $8 + 7 =$
3 $4 + 5 =$	**28** $9 + 8 =$	**53** $7 + 6 =$	**78** $3 + 12 =$
4 $7 + 6 =$	**29** $3 + 2 =$	**54** $14 + 4 =$	**79** $5 + 4 =$
5 $14 + 4 =$	**30** $4 + 15 =$	**55** $2 + 2 =$	**80** $9 + 8 =$
6 $5 + 15 =$	**31** $6 + 7 =$	**56** $6 + 5 =$	**81** $6 + 6 =$
7 $8 + 9 =$	**32** $5 + 4 =$	**57** $9 + 8 =$	**82** $2 + 12 =$
8 $12 + 2 =$	**33** $9 + 8 =$	**58** $14 + 5 =$	**83** $7 + 6 =$
9 $6 + 6 =$	**34** $7 + 6 =$	**59** $4 + 5 =$	**84** $4 + 5 =$
10 $2 + 3 =$	**35** $4 + 14 =$	**60** $13 + 3 =$	**85** $8 + 9 =$
11 $8 + 7 =$	**36** $10 + 10 =$	**61** $7 + 8 =$	**86** $4 + 14 =$
12 $4 + 5 =$	**37** $7 + 8 =$	**62** $10 + 9 =$	**87** $7 + 7 =$
13 $10 + 9 =$	**38** $15 + 4 =$	**63** $5 + 15 =$	**88** $10 + 9 =$
14 $2 + 3 =$	**39** $3 + 3 =$	**64** $4 + 4 =$	**89** $13 + 3 =$
15 $5 + 15 =$	**40** $5 + 14 =$	**65** $2 + 13 =$	**90** $2 + 11 =$
16 $7 + 7 =$	**41** $6 + 7 =$	**66** $6 + 7 =$	**91** $3 + 2 =$
17 $3 + 13 =$	**42** $1 + 1 =$	**67** $3 + 13 =$	**92** $5 + 15 =$
18 $6 + 7 =$	**43** $10 + 9 =$	**68** $2 + 3 =$	**93** $7 + 7 =$
19 $9 + 8 =$	**44** $13 + 3 =$	**69** $8 + 9 =$	**94** $8 + 8 =$
20 $4 + 3 =$	**45** $4 + 5 =$	**70** $2 + 12 =$	**95** $6 + 7 =$
21 $7 + 8 =$	**46** $15 + 4 =$	**71** $2 + 3 =$	**96** $7 + 8 =$
22 $8 + 8 =$	**47** $13 + 4 =$	**72** $14 + 3 =$	**97** $4 + 5 =$
23 $4 + 15 =$	**48** $8 + 9 =$	**73** $5 + 5 =$	**98** $2 + 11 =$
24 $8 + 9 =$	**49** $4 + 14 =$	**74** $3 + 14 =$	**99** $4 + 13 =$
25 $5 + 4 =$	**50** $2 + 12 =$	**75** $8 + 7 =$	**100** $9 + 9 =$

Time?	Time?	Time?	Time?
Try to be even quicker next time?	How are you doing?	Try to be faster?	Did you beat your target?

Exercise 17A	Exercise 17B	Exercise 17C	Exercise 17D
Name:	Name:	Name:	Name:
Date:	Date:	Date:	Date:

1. $7 + 10 =$	26. $10 + 8 =$	51. $0 + 2 =$	76. $1 + 18 =$
2. $6 + 1 =$	27. $20 + 0 =$	52. $18 + 1 =$	77. $3 + 10 =$
3. $0 + 8 =$	28. $1 + 12 =$	53. $10 + 6 =$	78. $0 + 17 =$
4. $10 + 6 =$	29. $19 + 1 =$	54. $3 + 1 =$	79. $6 + 1 =$
5. $11 + 1 =$	30. $0 + 11 =$	55. $0 + 17 =$	80. $10 + 5 =$
6. $0 + 16 =$	31. $9 + 10 =$	56. $5 + 10 =$	81. $16 + 0 =$
7. $10 + 7 =$	32. $0 + 18 =$	57. $1 + 4 =$	82. $1 + 15 =$
8. $10 + 4 =$	33. $7 + 10 =$	58. $16 + 0 =$	83. $7 + 10 =$
9. $13 + 0 =$	34. $1 + 17 =$	59. $10 + 5 =$	84. $0 + 16 =$
10. $1 + 9 =$	35. $10 + 10 =$	60. $15 + 0 =$	85. $14 + 1 =$
11. $1 + 10 =$	36. $0 + 16 =$	61. $10 + 6 =$	86. $10 + 9 =$
12. $0 + 12 =$	37. $9 + 1 =$	62. $14 + 1 =$	87. $18 + 0 =$
13. $10 + 5 =$	38. $0 + 8 =$	63. $1 + 7 =$	88. $1 + 1 =$
14. $14 + 0 =$	39. $7 + 10 =$	64. $4 + 10 =$	89. $2 + 10 =$
15. $1 + 15 =$	40. $1 + 15 =$	65. $0 + 19 =$	90. $0 + 3 =$
16. $10 + 6 =$	41. $6 + 1 =$	66. $10 + 2 =$	91. $13 + 1 =$
17. $18 + 0 =$	42. $0 + 5 =$	67. $8 + 0 =$	92. $10 + 4 =$
18. $1 + 7 =$	43. $4 + 10 =$	68. $13 + 1 =$	93. $12 + 0 =$
19. $3 + 1 =$	44. $1 + 14 =$	69. $1 + 9 =$	94. $1 + 5 =$
20. $0 + 19 =$	45. $3 + 0 =$	70. $0 + 20 =$	95. $6 + 10 =$
21. $2 + 10 =$	46. $10 + 2 =$	71. $10 + 10 =$	96. $0 + 7 =$
22. $1 + 8 =$	47. $1 + 10 =$	72. $10 + 2 =$	97. $11 + 1 =$
23. $20 + 0 =$	48. $1 + 13 =$	73. $11 + 0 =$	98. $10 + 8 =$
24. $10 + 9 =$	49. $12 + 0 =$	74. $1 + 12 =$	99. $10 + 0 =$
25. $6 + 10 =$	50. $10 + 1 =$	75. $3 + 10 =$	100. $1 + 9 =$

Time?	Time?	Time?	Time?

Do you think you are improving?

Are the facts at your fingertips?

Try to really focus!

Try to be faster?

Exercise 18A	Exercise 18B	Exercise 18C	Exercise 18D
Name:	Name:	Name:	Name:
Date:	Date:	Date:	Date:

1 $6 + 1 =$	**26** $10 + 7 =$	**51** $1 + 19 =$	**76** $0 + 20 =$
2 $0 + 7 =$	**27** $13 + 1 =$	**52** $11 + 0 =$	**77** $15 + 2 =$
3 $10 + 4 =$	**28** $0 + 12 =$	**53** $2 + 17 =$	**78** $10 + 6 =$
4 $7 + 2 =$	**29** $15 + 2 =$	**54** $10 + 10 =$	**79** $19 + 1 =$
5 $1 + 8 =$	**30** $10 + 6 =$	**55** $9 + 1 =$	**80** $11 + 0 =$
6 $18 + 0 =$	**31** $1 + 10 =$	**56** $4 + 0 =$	**81** $2 + 18 =$
7 $10 + 9 =$	**32** $14 + 0 =$	**57** $2 + 18 =$	**82** $7 + 10 =$
8 $9 + 2 =$	**33** $2 + 11 =$	**58** $8 + 10 =$	**83** $17 + 1 =$
9 $1 + 17 =$	**34** $5 + 10 =$	**59** $5 + 1 =$	**84** $0 + 3 =$
10 $10 + 0 =$	**35** $1 + 8 =$	**60** $0 + 12 =$	**85** $16 + 2 =$
11 $10 + 8 =$	**36** $16 + 0 =$	**61** $7 + 2 =$	**86** $10 + 8 =$
12 $11 + 2 =$	**37** $2 + 9 =$	**62** $10 + 6 =$	**87** $5 + 1 =$
13 $1 + 12 =$	**38** $4 + 10 =$	**63** $6 + 1 =$	**88** $0 + 15 =$
14 $0 + 19 =$	**39** $1 + 7 =$	**64** $0 + 16 =$	**89** $14 + 2 =$
15 $10 + 10 =$	**40** $17 + 0 =$	**65** $5 + 2 =$	**90** $10 + 9 =$
16 $13 + 2 =$	**41** $2 + 6 =$	**66** $7 + 10 =$	**91** $7 + 1 =$
17 $1 + 9 =$	**42** $3 + 10 =$	**67** $1 + 8 =$	**92** $9 + 0 =$
18 $14 + 0 =$	**43** $18 + 1 =$	**68** $0 + 13 =$	**93** $2 + 13 =$
19 $10 + 8 =$	**44** $0 + 2 =$	**69** $4 + 2 =$	**94** $5 + 10 =$
20 $15 + 2 =$	**45** $2 + 4 =$	**70** $10 + 9 =$	**95** $1 + 2 =$
21 $1 + 7 =$	**46** $2 + 10 =$	**71** $3 + 1 =$	**96** $10 + 0 =$
22 $20 + 0 =$	**47** $1 + 5 =$	**72** $1 + 0 =$	**97** $2 + 12 =$
23 $10 + 7 =$	**48** $0 + 3 =$	**73** $2 + 15 =$	**98** $4 + 10 =$
24 $16 + 2 =$	**49** $1 + 2 =$	**74** $2 + 10 =$	**99** $1 + 11 =$
25 $1 + 6 =$	**50** $10 + 1 =$	**75** $1 + 14 =$	**100** $3 + 0 =$

Time?	Time?	Time?	Time?
What is your time?	How did you do?	Is this your fastest time?	Did you reach your target?

Exercise 19A	Exercise 19B	Exercise 19C	Exercise 19D
Name:	Name:	Name:	Name:
Date:	Date:	Date:	Date:

1 $7 + 1 =$	**26** $19 + 1 =$	**51** $10 + 7 =$	**76** $13 + 1 =$
2 $10 + 0 =$	**27** $11 + 7 =$	**52** $14 + 2 =$	**77** $10 + 8 =$
3 $10 + 7 =$	**28** $13 + 0 =$	**53** $1 + 19 =$	**78** $6 + 11 =$
4 $14 + 2 =$	**29** $2 + 11 =$	**54** $7 + 11 =$	**79** $2 + 14 =$
5 $11 + 7 =$	**30** $6 + 10 =$	**55** $10 + 8 =$	**80** $9 + 11 =$
6 $1 + 15 =$	**31** $11 + 5 =$	**56** $2 + 18 =$	**81** $0 + 20 =$
7 $10 + 0 =$	**32** $18 + 1 =$	**57** $11 + 9 =$	**82** $10 + 4 =$
8 $10 + 9 =$	**33** $0 + 4 =$	**58** $8 + 10 =$	**83** $2 + 15 =$
9 $8 + 2 =$	**34** $10 + 10 =$	**59** $11 + 6 =$	**84** $7 + 10 =$
10 $11 + 7 =$	**35** $14 + 2 =$	**60** $0 + 10 =$	**85** $12 + 1 =$
11 $16 + 1 =$	**36** $9 + 11 =$	**61** $17 + 2 =$	**86** $11 + 6 =$
12 $20 + 0 =$	**37** $10 + 7 =$	**62** $10 + 5 =$	**87** $15 + 2 =$
13 $10 + 6 =$	**38** $12 + 0 =$	**63** $11 + 4 =$	**88** $8 + 0 =$
14 $5 + 2 =$	**39** $1 + 9 =$	**64** $16 + 1 =$	**89** $10 + 9 =$
15 $11 + 4 =$	**40** $6 + 11 =$	**65** $11 + 2 =$	**90** $7 + 11 =$
16 $1 + 17 =$	**41** $2 + 3 =$	**66** $11 + 3 =$	**91** $2 + 16 =$
17 $0 + 19 =$	**42** $15 + 0 =$	**67** $9 + 10 =$	**92** $1 + 17 =$
18 $3 + 10 =$	**43** $1 + 5 =$	**68** $0 + 12 =$	**93** $10 + 6 =$
19 $11 + 5 =$	**44** $4 + 10 =$	**69** $2 + 15 =$	**94** $8 + 11 =$
20 $9 + 2 =$	**45** $11 + 3 =$	**70** $10 + 8 =$	**95** $2 + 17 =$
21 $8 + 11 =$	**46** $16 + 2 =$	**71** $0 + 14 =$	**96** $11 + 4 =$
22 $2 + 7 =$	**47** $0 + 18 =$	**72** $7 + 11 =$	**97** $0 + 19 =$
23 $6 + 10 =$	**48** $17 + 1 =$	**73** $9 + 2 =$	**98** $10 + 7 =$
24 $0 + 14 =$	**49** $10 + 6 =$	**74** $11 + 7 =$	**99** $2 + 18 =$
25 $1 + 18 =$	**50** $8 + 11 =$	**75** $1 + 13 =$	**100** $6 + 11 =$

Time?	Time?	Time?	Time?
How well did you do?	Have you reached your target?	Can you be faster?	What is your time?

Exercise 20A	Exercise 20B	Exercise 20C	Exercise 20D
Name:	Name:	Name:	Name:
Date:	Date:	Date:	Date:

#	20A	#	20B	#	20C	#	20D
1	1 + 7 =	26	10 + 3 =	51	12 + 6 =	76	10 + 5 =
2	0 + 14 =	27	1 + 10 =	52	8 + 11 =	77	7 + 12 =
3	7 + 10 =	28	7 + 11 =	53	10 + 7 =	78	11 + 8 =
4	6 + 2 =	29	10 + 7 =	54	13 + 1 =	79	9 + 2 =
5	4 + 11 =	30	6 + 12 =	55	2 + 9 =	80	1 + 9 =
6	12 + 7 =	31	13 + 0 =	56	12 + 6 =	81	2 + 10 =
7	6 + 10 =	32	11 + 9 =	57	8 + 11 =	82	6 + 10 =
8	1 + 8 =	33	1 + 10 =	58	0 + 14 =	83	12 + 8 =
9	2 + 15 =	34	12 + 4 =	59	10 + 5 =	84	1 + 0 =
10	7 + 11 =	35	8 + 2 =	60	9 + 2 =	85	7 + 11 =
11	10 + 2 =	36	1 + 5 =	61	11 + 6 =	86	12 + 2 =
12	14 + 0 =	37	8 + 12 =	62	6 + 10 =	87	11 + 5 =
13	12 + 8 =	38	11 + 7 =	63	1 + 15 =	88	4 + 10 =
14	16 + 2 =	39	9 + 10 =	64	4 + 11 =	89	8 + 1 =
15	11 + 3 =	40	2 + 9 =	65	12 + 3 =	90	2 + 3 =
16	4 + 12 =	41	0 + 10 =	66	7 + 10 =	91	6 + 11 =
17	10 + 5 =	42	6 + 12 =	67	2 + 18 =	92	10 + 9 =
18	9 + 1 =	43	11 + 6 =	68	8 + 11 =	93	5 + 12 =
19	12 + 6 =	44	7 + 10 =	69	10 + 3 =	94	0 + 8 =
20	13 + 2 =	45	9 + 1 =	70	16 + 0 =	95	11 + 7 =
21	10 + 7 =	46	2 + 7 =	71	5 + 12 =	96	4 + 10 =
22	2 + 11 =	47	6 + 11 =	72	11 + 8 =	97	6 + 2 =
23	0 + 6 =	48	12 + 5 =	73	7 + 10 =	98	5 + 1 =
24	7 + 12 =	49	0 + 14 =	74	12 + 6 =	99	12 + 3 =
25	11 + 9 =	50	5 + 10 =	75	17 + 2 =	100	4 + 12 =

Time?	Time?	Time?	Time?

Are the facts at your fingertips?

Try to really focus!

Which facts do you find the easiest?

Did you do well?

Exercise 21A	Exercise 21B	Exercise 21C	Exercise 21D
Name:	Name:	Name:	Name:
Date:	Date:	Date:	Date:

1 $7 + 11 =$	**26** $10 + 4 =$	**51** $9 + 5 =$	**76** $3 + 2 =$
2 $9 + 6 =$	**27** $2 + 1 =$	**52** $4 + 12 =$	**77** $9 + 7 =$
3 $0 + 7 =$	**28** $0 + 17 =$	**53** $11 + 5 =$	**78** $5 + 12 =$
4 $1 + 6 =$	**29** $3 + 10 =$	**54** $7 + 2 =$	**79** $11 + 6 =$
5 $10 + 4 =$	**30** $5 + 2 =$	**55** $10 + 6 =$	**80** $6 + 10 =$
6 $2 + 17 =$	**31** $11 + 4 =$	**56** $18 + 0 =$	**81** $0 + 4 =$
7 $12 + 6 =$	**32** $12 + 7 =$	**57** $6 + 1 =$	**82** $1 + 7 =$
8 $9 + 8 =$	**33** $6 + 9 =$	**58** $9 + 4 =$	**83** $4 + 9 =$
9 $7 + 12 =$	**34** $8 + 12 =$	**59** $12 + 6 =$	**84** $12 + 5 =$
10 $11 + 6 =$	**35** $7 + 11 =$	**60** $7 + 11 =$	**85** $8 + 11 =$
11 $5 + 2 =$	**36** $5 + 12 =$	**61** $17 + 2 =$	**86** $2 + 9 =$
12 $10 + 4 =$	**37** $2 + 8 =$	**62** $3 + 10 =$	**87** $10 + 10 =$
13 $3 + 0 =$	**38** $7 + 10 =$	**63** $0 + 9 =$	**88** $3 + 0 =$
14 $1 + 17 =$	**39** $11 + 0 =$	**64** $1 + 16 =$	**89** $9 + 1 =$
15 $6 + 9 =$	**40** $1 + 6 =$	**65** $3 + 9 =$	**90** $11 + 5 =$
16 $1 + 12 =$	**41** $8 + 12 =$	**66** $2 + 12 =$	**91** $4 + 9 =$
17 $2 + 13 =$	**42** $9 + 7 =$	**67** $11 + 7 =$	**92** $12 + 5 =$
18 $2 + 11 =$	**43** $9 + 11 =$	**68** $15 + 2 =$	**93** $6 + 10 =$
19 $10 + 5 =$	**44** $10 + 10 =$	**69** $10 + 8 =$	**94** $2 + 3 =$
20 $1 + 16 =$	**45** $16 + 0 =$	**70** $13 + 0 =$	**95** $9 + 6 =$
21 $0 + 14 =$	**46** $1 + 13 =$	**71** $1 + 14 =$	**96** $5 + 11 =$
22 $4 + 9 =$	**47** $9 + 11 =$	**72** $2 + 9 =$	**97** $7 + 12 =$
23 $11 + 6 =$	**48** $9 + 10 =$	**73** $11 + 6 =$	**98** $10 + 7 =$
24 $12 + 3 =$	**49** $6 + 11 =$	**74** $1 + 12 =$	**99** $8 + 2 =$
25 $2 + 15 =$	**50** $10 + 8 =$	**75** $10 + 3 =$	**100** $1 + 8 =$

Time?	Time?	Time?	Time?

Did you beat you score?

Which facts do you find the hardest?

Is this your best score?

Try to concentrate even more?

Exercise 22A	Exercise 22B	Exercise 22C	Exercise 22D
Name:	Name:	Name:	Name:
Date:	Date:	Date:	Date:

(1) $9 + 9 =$	(26) $7 + 12 =$	(51) $5 + 5 =$	(76) $11 + 6 =$
(2) $9 + 10 =$	(27) $11 + 7 =$	(52) $12 + 7 =$	(77) $6 + 10 =$
(3) $18 + 1 =$	(28) $18 + 2 =$	(53) $3 + 9 =$	(78) $2 + 2 =$
(4) $6 + 12 =$	(29) $8 + 8 =$	(54) $10 + 8 =$	(79) $12 + 5 =$
(5) $10 + 8 =$	(30) $0 + 13 =$	(55) $6 + 11 =$	(80) $5 + 9 =$
(6) $7 + 9 =$	(31) $6 + 12 =$	(56) $2 + 9 =$	(81) $11 + 7 =$
(7) $11 + 4 =$	(32) $10 + 6 =$	(57) $19 + 1 =$	(82) $4 + 12 =$
(8) $5 + 10 =$	(33) $5 + 9 =$	(58) $7 + 7 =$	(83) $8 + 8 =$
(9) $2 + 9 =$	(34) $11 + 4 =$	(59) $0 + 8 =$	(84) $10 + 8 =$
(10) $5 + 5 =$	(35) $17 + 2 =$	(60) $10 + 9 =$	(85) $17 + 2 =$
(11) $9 + 10 =$	(36) $1 + 14 =$	(61) $7 + 9 =$	(86) $9 + 6 =$
(12) $12 + 8 =$	(37) $12 + 5 =$	(62) $12 + 5 =$	(87) $12 + 3 =$
(13) $3 + 9 =$	(38) $3 + 10 =$	(63) $7 + 11 =$	(88) $6 + 6 =$
(14) $11 + 7 =$	(39) $9 + 4 =$	(64) $2 + 17 =$	(89) $2 + 11 =$
(15) $10 + 2 =$	(40) $3 + 3 =$	(65) $15 + 0 =$	(90) $10 + 8 =$
(16) $10 + 1 =$	(41) $11 + 2 =$	(66) $1 + 8 =$	(91) $6 + 2 =$
(17) $6 + 12 =$	(42) $16 + 2 =$	(67) $9 + 10 =$	(92) $9 + 8 =$
(18) $9 + 5 =$	(43) $0 + 19 =$	(68) $4 + 4 =$	(93) $5 + 2 =$
(19) $11 + 2 =$	(44) $1 + 15 =$	(69) $12 + 3 =$	(94) $11 + 7 =$
(20) $2 + 3 =$	(45) $10 + 7 =$	(70) $6 + 11 =$	(95) $2 + 12 =$
(21) $0 + 16 =$	(46) $3 + 9 =$	(71) $9 + 5 =$	(96) $10 + 4 =$
(22) $6 + 6 =$	(47) $12 + 6 =$	(72) $13 + 2 =$	(97) $10 + 10 =$
(23) $10 + 8 =$	(48) $1 + 11 =$	(73) $9 + 9 =$	(98) $5 + 9 =$
(24) $15 + 1 =$	(49) $2 + 2 =$	(74) $9 + 6 =$	(99) $2 + 6 =$
(25) $4 + 9 =$	(50) $7 + 7 =$	(75) $14 + 2 =$	(100) $3 + 12 =$

Time?	Time?	Time?	Time?

Is this your best score yet?

Did you beat your target?

Have you reached your target yet?

How do you think you are doing?

Exercise 23A	Exercise 23B	Exercise 23C	Exercise 23D
Name:	Name:	Name:	Name:
Date:	Date:	Date:	Date:

#	23A	#	23B	#	23C	#	23D
1	7 + 11 =	26	4 + 3 =	51	10 + 4 =	76	2 + 3 =
2	2 + 17 =	27	10 + 9 =	52	2 + 12 =	77	6 + 5 =
3	15 + 0 =	28	7 + 9 =	53	11 + 7 =	78	11 + 2 =
4	1 + 8 =	29	12 + 5 =	54	6 + 5 =	79	9 + 5 =
5	9 + 10 =	30	8 + 9 =	55	5 + 2 =	80	6 + 12 =
6	3 + 4 =	31	7 + 11 =	56	9 + 8 =	81	10 + 1 =
7	4 + 4 =	32	2 + 17 =	57	6 + 2 =	82	11 + 7 =
8	12 + 3 =	33	15 + 0 =	58	10 + 8 =	83	3 + 9 =
9	6 + 11 =	34	1 + 8 =	59	2 + 11 =	84	12 + 8 =
10	9 + 5 =	35	6 + 5 =	60	4 + 3 =	85	9 + 10 =
11	13 + 2 =	36	9 + 10 =	61	6 + 6 =	86	4 + 3 =
12	9 + 9 =	37	4 + 4 =	62	12 + 3 =	87	5 + 5 =
13	9 + 6 =	38	12 + 3 =	63	9 + 6 =	88	2 + 9 =
14	14 + 2 =	39	6 + 11 =	64	17 + 2 =	89	5 + 10 =
15	5 + 6 =	40	9 + 5 =	65	10 + 8 =	90	11 + 4 =
16	5 + 5 =	41	13 + 2 =	66	7 + 8 =	91	7 + 9 =
17	12 + 7 =	42	3 + 4 =	67	8 + 8 =	92	16 + 1 =
18	3 + 9 =	43	9 + 9 =	68	4 + 12 =	93	6 + 12 =
19	10 + 8 =	44	9 + 6 =	69	11 + 7 =	94	18 + 1 =
20	6 + 11 =	45	14 + 2 =	70	5 + 9 =	95	9 + 9 =
21	2 + 9 =	46	3 + 12 =	71	12 + 5 =	96	2 + 3 =
22	19 + 1 =	47	2 + 6 =	72	2 + 12 =	97	7 + 9 =
23	7 + 7 =	48	5 + 9 =	73	6 + 10 =	98	19 + 1 =
24	0 + 8 =	49	10 + 10 =	74	11 + 6 =	99	6 + 11 =
25	9 + 8 =	50	8 + 7 =	75	2 + 7 =	100	7 + 8 =

Time?	Time?	Time?	Time?

Try to be even quicker next time!

Can you try to be faster?

Did you do well?

What have you learnt today?

Exercise 24A	Exercise 24B	Exercise 24C	Exercise 24D
Name:	Name:	Name:	Name:
Date:	Date:	Date:	Date:

1 $2 + 12 =$	**26** $14 + 5 =$	**51** $5 + 15 =$	**76** $11 + 1 =$
2 $6 + 5 =$	**27** $16 + 1 =$	**52** $7 + 11 =$	**77** $13 + 2 =$
3 $5 + 2 =$	**28** $7 + 9 =$	**53** $2 + 17 =$	**78** $3 + 4 =$
4 $9 + 8 =$	**29** $15 + 5 =$	**54** $15 + 0 =$	**79** $3 + 14 =$
5 $4 + 14 =$	**30** $11 + 4 =$	**55** $4 + 14 =$	**80** $8 + 8 =$
6 $6 + 2 =$	**31** $5 + 10 =$	**56** $3 + 4 =$	**81** $15 + 5 =$
7 $10 + 8 =$	**32** $2 + 9 =$	**57** $12 + 3 =$	**82** $9 + 6 =$
8 $11 + 2 =$	**33** $5 + 5 =$	**58** $4 + 15 =$	**83** $14 + 2 =$
9 $4 + 3 =$	**34** $13 + 3 =$	**59** $6 + 11 =$	**84** $3 + 12 =$
10 $6 + 6 =$	**35** $4 + 3 =$	**60** $4 + 4 =$	**85** $2 + 13 =$
11 $1 + 11 =$	**36** $9 + 10 =$	**61** $9 + 5 =$	**86** $2 + 6 =$
12 $12 + 3 =$	**37** $12 + 8 =$	**62** $13 + 2 =$	**87** $5 + 9 =$
13 $9 + 6 =$	**38** $3 + 9 =$	**63** $2 + 13 =$	**88** $10 + 10 =$
14 $12 + 3 =$	**39** $12 + 2 =$	**64** $9 + 9 =$	**89** $12 + 2 =$
15 $17 + 2 =$	**40** $11 + 7 =$	**65** $9 + 6 =$	**90** $8 + 7 =$
16 $10 + 8 =$	**41** $10 + 1 =$	**66** $3 + 13 =$	**91** $17 + 2 =$
17 $5 + 15 =$	**42** $15 + 4 =$	**67** $14 + 2 =$	**92** $5 + 14 =$
18 $7 + 8 =$	**43** $6 + 12 =$	**68** $5 + 6 =$	**93** $8 + 9 =$
19 $8 + 8 =$	**44** $9 + 5 =$	**69** $5 + 5 =$	**94** $13 + 3 =$
20 $4 + 12 =$	**45** $11 + 2 =$	**70** $12 + 7 =$	**95** $12 + 3 =$
21 $13 + 4 =$	**46** $11 + 1 =$	**71** $3 + 9 =$	**96** $9 + 6 =$
22 $11 + 7 =$	**47** $6 + 5 =$	**72** $10 + 8 =$	**97** $1 + 12 =$
23 $5 + 9 =$	**48** $2 + 3 =$	**73** $6 + 11 =$	**98** $5 + 2 =$
24 $3 + 13 =$	**49** $6 + 9 =$	**74** $2 + 12 =$	**99** $14 + 4 =$
25 $12 + 5 =$	**50** $3 + 14 =$	**75** $2 + 9 =$	**100** $11 + 7 =$

Time?	Time?	Time?	Time?
Did you use strategies?	Where can you improve?	Are you improving?	Did you do well?

Exercise 25A	Exercise 25B	Exercise 25C	Exercise 25D
Name:	Name:	Name:	Name:
Date:	Date:	Date:	Date:

#		#		#		#	
1	13 + 3 =	26	4 + 7 =	51	14 + 2 =	76	9 + 6 =
2	4 + 3 =	27	7 + 9 =	52	6 + 8 =	77	3 + 5 =
3	9 + 10 =	28	4 + 15 =	53	3 + 12 =	78	14 + 2 =
4	7 + 4 =	29	15 + 5 =	54	2 + 13 =	79	3 + 12 =
5	12 + 8 =	30	11 + 4 =	55	2 + 6 =	80	2 + 13 =
6	3 + 9 =	31	3 + 8 =	56	5 + 9 =	81	6 + 2 =
7	12 + 2 =	32	6 + 11 =	57	10 + 10 =	82	4 + 7 =
8	11 + 7 =	33	4 + 4 =	58	12 + 2 =	83	5 + 9 =
9	10 + 1 =	34	9 + 5 =	59	8 + 7 =	84	10 + 10 =
10	15 + 4 =	35	13 + 2 =	60	17 + 2 =	85	12 + 2 =
11	6 + 12 =	36	2 + 16 =	61	5 + 14 =	86	8 + 7 =
12	3 + 8 =	37	3 + 5 =	62	9 + 6 =	87	17 + 2 =
13	9 + 5 =	38	9 + 9 =	63	13 + 3 =	88	5 + 4 =
14	2 + 11 =	39	9 + 6 =	64	5 + 7 =	89	9 + 6 =
15	6 + 5 =	40	5 + 6 =	65	12 + 3 =	90	13 + 3 =
16	2 + 3 =	41	5 + 5 =	66	9 + 6 =	91	6 + 3 =
17	6 + 9 =	42	12 + 7 =	67	1 + 12 =	92	12 + 3 =
18	3 + 14 =	43	7 + 5 =	68	5 + 2 =	93	9 + 6 =
19	6 + 11 =	44	3 + 9 =	69	14 + 4 =	94	11 + 7 =
20	8 + 4 =	45	10 + 8 =	70	11 + 7 =	95	14 + 4 =
21	4 + 4 =	46	6 + 11 =	71	4 + 7 =	96	5 + 2 =
22	9 + 5 =	47	4 + 7 =	72	8 + 8 =	97	9 + 6 =
23	13 + 2 =	48	2 + 12 =	73	4 + 3 =	98	7 + 8 =
24	9 + 6 =	49	2 + 9 =	74	3 + 9 =	99	9 + 1 =
25	8 + 6 =	50	6 + 8 =	75	6 + 12 =	100	8 + 5 =

Time?	Time?	Time?	Time?

How did you do?

Did you beat your best score?

Can you try to be faster?

Have you reached your target?

Exercise 26A

Name:
Date:

1. $\Box + 1 = 9$
2. $0 + \Box = 7$
3. $\Box + 1 = 13$
4. $1 + \Box = 3$
5. $1 + \Box = 6$
6. $\Box + 1 = 15$
7. $\Box + 19 = 19$
8. $16 + \Box = 17$
9. $\Box + 18 = 19$
10. $1 + \Box = 2$
11. $11 + \Box = 11$
12. $\Box + 5 = 6$
13. $18 + \Box = 18$
14. $\Box + 13 = 14$
15. $1 + \Box = 12$
16. $\Box + 9 = 9$
17. $1 + \Box = 18$
18. $\Box + 1 = 4$
19. $16 + \Box = 16$
20. $6 + \Box = 7$
21. $\Box + 8 = 9$
22. $9 + \Box = 10$
23. $\Box + 12 = 12$
24. $1 + \Box = 16$
25. $\Box + 8 = 8$

Time?

How do you think you are doing?

Exercise 26B

Name:
Date:

26. $3 + \Box = 4$
27. $\Box + 1 = 15$
28. $8 + \Box = 8$
29. $\Box + 1 = 18$
30. $0 + \Box = 7$
31. $\Box + 1 = 8$
32. $1 + \Box = 7$
33. $12 + \Box = 13$
34. $\Box + 19 = 20$
35. $17 + \Box = 17$
36. $1 + \Box = 9$
37. $\Box + 14 = 14$
38. $1 + \Box = 5$
39. $\Box + 9 = 10$
40. $18 + \Box = 19$
41. $\Box + 13 = 13$
42. $18 + \Box = 19$
43. $\Box + 0 = 2$
44. $8 + \Box = 9$
45. $10 + \Box = 11$
46. $\Box + 5 = 5$
47. $1 + \Box = 15$
48. $13 + \Box = 14$
49. $\Box + 6 = 6$
50. $14 + \Box = 15$

Time?

How did you do?

Exercise 26C

Name:
Date:

51. $10 + \Box = 11$
52. $\Box + 3 = 4$
53. $9 + \Box = 9$
54. $\Box + 4 = 5$
55. $12 + \Box = 12$
56. $\Box + 17 = 18$
57. $\Box + 0 = 7$
58. $1 + \Box = 16$
59. $\Box + 2 = 3$
60. $10 + \Box = 10$
61. $18 + \Box = 19$
62. $\Box + 11 = 12$
63. $11 + \Box = 11$
64. $\Box + 8 = 9$
65. $19 + \Box = 20$
66. $17 + \Box = 17$
67. $\Box + 1 = 2$
68. $12 + \Box = 13$
69. $\Box + 9 = 10$
70. $5 + \Box = 5$
71. $\Box + 1 = 15$
72. $12 + \Box = 13$
73. $\Box + 9 = 9$
74. $4 + \Box = 5$
75. $\Box + 11 = 11$

Time?

Is this your best score?

Exercise 26D

Name:
Date:

76. $10 + \Box = 11$
77. $\Box + 5 = 5$
78. $1 + \Box = 19$
79. $3 + \Box = 3$
80. $\Box + 3 = 4$
81. $5 + \Box = 6$
82. $0 + \Box = 20$
83. $\Box + 17 = 18$
84. $16 + \Box = 16$
85. $\Box + 1 = 8$
86. $3 + \Box = 4$
87. $\Box + 5 = 6$
88. $0 + \Box = 17$
89. $9 + \Box = 10$
90. $\Box + 0 = 5$
91. $8 + \Box = 9$
92. $\Box + 17 = 17$
93. $2 + \Box = 3$
94. $\Box + 1 = 7$
95. $8 + \Box = 9$
96. $14 + \Box = 15$
97. $\Box + 20 = 20$
98. $17 + \Box = 18$
99. $\Box + 0 = 6$
100. $\Box + 3 = 4$

Time?

Which facts do you find the easiest?

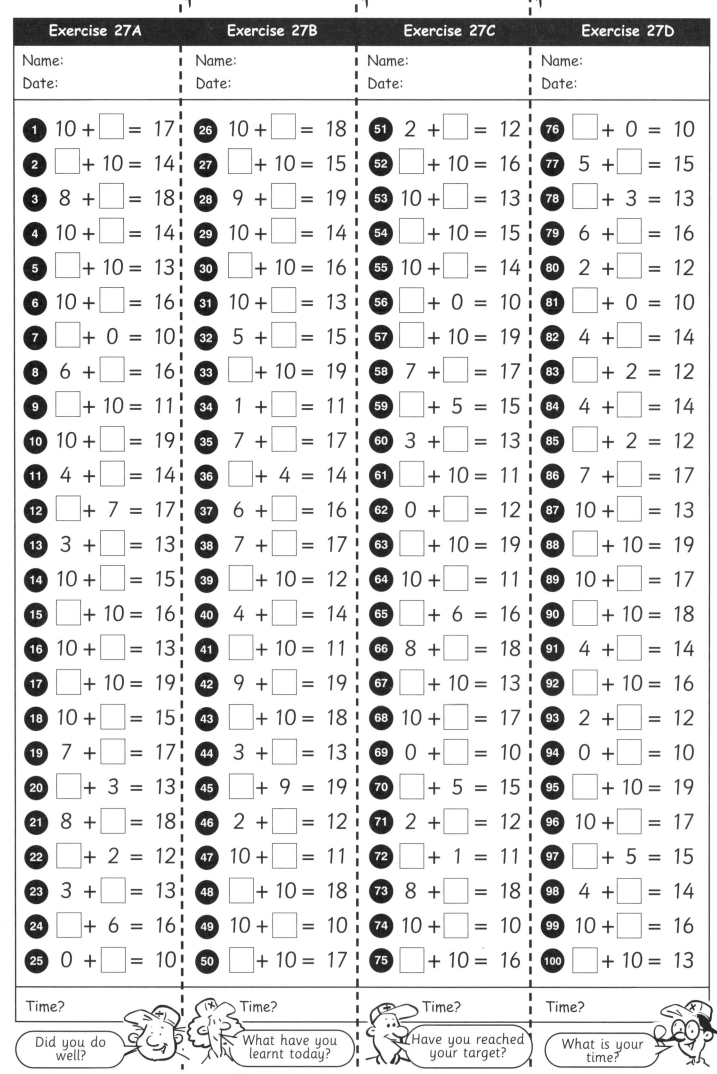

Exercise 27A	Exercise 27B	Exercise 27C	Exercise 27D
Name:	Name:	Name:	Name:
Date:	Date:	Date:	Date:

Exercise 27A

1. $10 + \square = 17$
2. $\square + 10 = 14$
3. $8 + \square = 18$
4. $10 + \square = 14$
5. $\square + 10 = 13$
6. $10 + \square = 16$
7. $\square + 0 = 10$
8. $6 + \square = 16$
9. $\square + 10 = 11$
10. $10 + \square = 19$
11. $4 + \square = 14$
12. $\square + 7 = 17$
13. $3 + \square = 13$
14. $10 + \square = 15$
15. $\square + 10 = 16$
16. $10 + \square = 13$
17. $\square + 10 = 19$
18. $10 + \square = 15$
19. $7 + \square = 17$
20. $\square + 3 = 13$
21. $8 + \square = 18$
22. $\square + 2 = 12$
23. $3 + \square = 13$
24. $\square + 6 = 16$
25. $0 + \square = 10$

Exercise 27B

26. $10 + \square = 18$
27. $\square + 10 = 15$
28. $9 + \square = 19$
29. $10 + \square = 14$
30. $\square + 10 = 16$
31. $10 + \square = 13$
32. $5 + \square = 15$
33. $\square + 10 = 19$
34. $1 + \square = 11$
35. $7 + \square = 17$
36. $\square + 4 = 14$
37. $6 + \square = 16$
38. $7 + \square = 17$
39. $\square + 10 = 12$
40. $4 + \square = 14$
41. $\square + 10 = 11$
42. $9 + \square = 19$
43. $\square + 10 = 18$
44. $3 + \square = 13$
45. $\square + 9 = 19$
46. $2 + \square = 12$
47. $10 + \square = 11$
48. $\square + 10 = 18$
49. $10 + \square = 10$
50. $\square + 10 = 17$

Exercise 27C

51. $2 + \square = 12$
52. $\square + 10 = 16$
53. $10 + \square = 13$
54. $\square + 10 = 15$
55. $10 + \square = 14$
56. $\square + 0 = 10$
57. $\square + 10 = 19$
58. $7 + \square = 17$
59. $\square + 5 = 15$
60. $3 + \square = 13$
61. $\square + 10 = 11$
62. $0 + \square = 12$
63. $\square + 10 = 19$
64. $10 + \square = 11$
65. $\square + 6 = 16$
66. $8 + \square = 18$
67. $\square + 10 = 13$
68. $10 + \square = 17$
69. $0 + \square = 10$
70. $\square + 5 = 15$
71. $2 + \square = 12$
72. $\square + 1 = 11$
73. $8 + \square = 18$
74. $10 + \square = 10$
75. $\square + 10 = 16$

Exercise 27D

76. $\square + 0 = 10$
77. $5 + \square = 15$
78. $\square + 3 = 13$
79. $6 + \square = 16$
80. $2 + \square = 12$
81. $\square + 0 = 10$
82. $4 + \square = 14$
83. $\square + 2 = 12$
84. $4 + \square = 14$
85. $\square + 2 = 12$
86. $7 + \square = 17$
87. $10 + \square = 13$
88. $\square + 10 = 19$
89. $10 + \square = 17$
90. $\square + 10 = 18$
91. $4 + \square = 14$
92. $\square + 10 = 16$
93. $2 + \square = 12$
94. $0 + \square = 10$
95. $\square + 10 = 19$
96. $10 + \square = 17$
97. $\square + 5 = 15$
98. $4 + \square = 14$
99. $10 + \square = 16$
100. $\square + 10 = 13$

Time? | Time? | Time? | Time?

Did you do well?
What have you learnt today?
Have you reached your target?
What is your time?

Exercise 28A	Exercise 28B	Exercise 28C	Exercise 28D
Name:	Name:	Name:	Name:
Date:	Date:	Date:	Date:

1 $2 + \boxed{} = 20$

2 $\boxed{} + 2 = 13$

3 $\boxed{} + 14 = 16$

4 $2 + \boxed{} = 12$

5 $\boxed{} + 2 = 18$

6 $10 + \boxed{} = 12$

7 $\boxed{} + 12 = 14$

8 $2 + \boxed{} = 16$

9 $17 + \boxed{} = 19$

10 $\boxed{} + 15 = 17$

11 $1 + \boxed{} = 3$

12 $\boxed{} + 2 = 9$

13 $\boxed{} + 2 = 13$

14 $9 + \boxed{} = 11$

15 $13 + \boxed{} = 15$

16 $\boxed{} + 8 = 10$

17 $\boxed{} + 9 = 11$

18 $2 + \boxed{} = 15$

19 $15 + \boxed{} = 17$

20 $\boxed{} + 2 = 8$

21 $\boxed{} + 3 = 5$

22 $7 + \boxed{} = 9$

23 $2 + \boxed{} = 12$

24 $\boxed{} + 2 = 16$

25 $2 + \boxed{} = 18$

26 $\boxed{} + 2 = 15$

27 $1 + \boxed{} = 3$

28 $\boxed{} + 18 = 20$

29 $\boxed{} + 7 = 9$

30 $13 + \boxed{} = 15$

31 $2 + \boxed{} = 13$

32 $\boxed{} + 2 = 14$

33 $2 + \boxed{} = 17$

34 $\boxed{} + 2 = 10$

35 $\boxed{} + 3 = 5$

36 $12 + \boxed{} = 14$

37 $2 + \boxed{} = 19$

38 $\boxed{} + 6 = 8$

39 $2 + \boxed{} = 9$

40 $\boxed{} + 2 = 18$

41 $2 + \boxed{} = 14$

42 $\boxed{} + 2 = 15$

43 $2 + \boxed{} = 13$

44 $\boxed{} + 2 = 19$

45 $2 + \boxed{} = 17$

46 $2 + \boxed{} = 9$

47 $\boxed{} + 2 = 3$

48 $2 + \boxed{} = 13$

49 $2 + \boxed{} = 11$

50 $\boxed{} + 2 = 12$

51 $\boxed{} + 16 = 18$

52 $2 + \boxed{} = 16$

53 $2 + \boxed{} = 8$

54 $\boxed{} + 2 = 4$

55 $2 + \boxed{} = 11$

56 $\boxed{} + 10 = 12$

57 $2 + \boxed{} = 18$

58 $\boxed{} + 13 = 15$

59 $\boxed{} + 2 = 8$

60 $2 + \boxed{} = 14$

61 $\boxed{} + 2 = 2$

62 $2 + \boxed{} = 20$

63 $2 + \boxed{} = 18$

64 $\boxed{} + 14 = 16$

65 $2 + \boxed{} = 13$

66 $\boxed{} + 2 = 19$

67 $2 + \boxed{} = 16$

68 $\boxed{} + 2 = 11$

69 $\boxed{} + 2 = 5$

70 $2 + \boxed{} = 3$

71 $2 + \boxed{} = 19$

72 $\boxed{} + 14 = 16$

73 $\boxed{} + 2 = 14$

74 $2 + \boxed{} = 10$

75 $2 + \boxed{} = 8$

76 $\boxed{} + 2 = 16$

77 $2 + \boxed{} = 9$

78 $\boxed{} + 2 = 17$

79 $2 + \boxed{} = 8$

80 $\boxed{} + 2 = 15$

81 $2 + \boxed{} = 5$

82 $2 + \boxed{} = 19$

83 $\boxed{} + 2 = 15$

84 $2 + \boxed{} = 8$

85 $\boxed{} + 2 = 6$

86 $\boxed{} + 2 = 11$

87 $2 + \boxed{} = 18$

88 $2 + \boxed{} = 16$

89 $\boxed{} + 2 = 15$

90 $2 + \boxed{} = 11$

91 $\boxed{} + 13 = 15$

92 $2 + \boxed{} = 14$

93 $18 + \boxed{} = 20$

94 $\boxed{} + 2 = 18$

95 $\boxed{} + 2 = 9$

96 $2 + \boxed{} = 2$

97 $\boxed{} + 2 = 20$

98 $\boxed{} + 13 = 15$

99 $11 + \boxed{} = 13$

100 $\boxed{} + 2 = 11$

Time? Time? Time? Time?

Try to be even quicker next time?

How are you doing?

Try to be faster?

Did you beat your target?

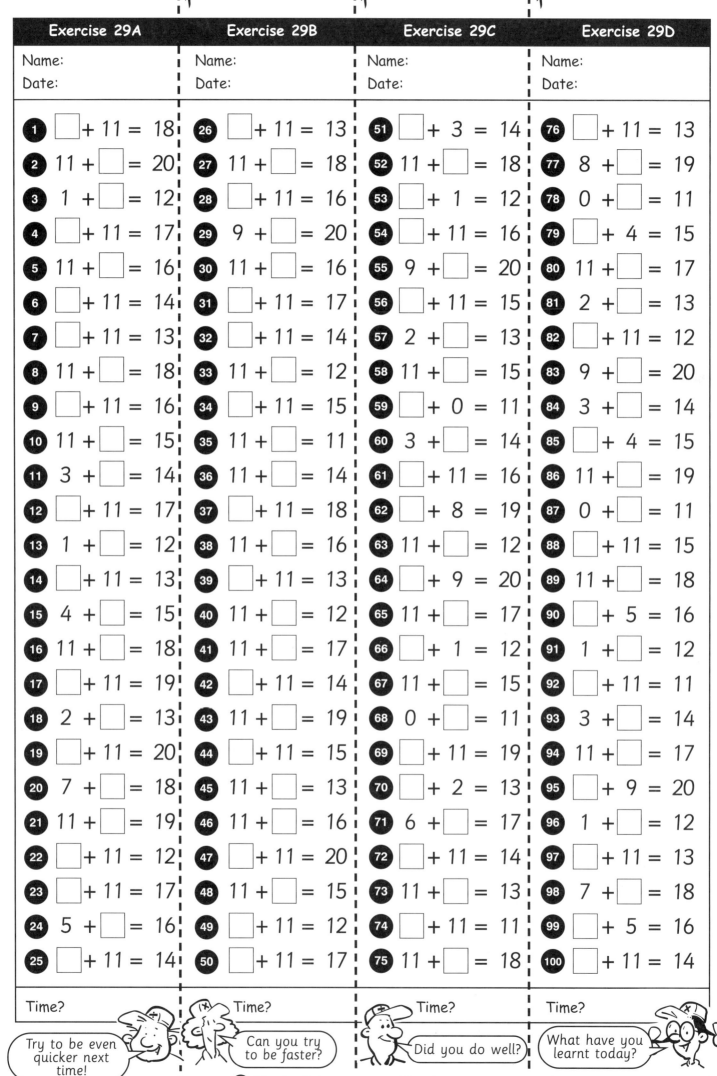

Exercise 29A	Exercise 29B	Exercise 29C	Exercise 29D
Name:	Name:	Name:	Name:
Date:	Date:	Date:	Date:

Exercise 29A

1. ☐ + 11 = 18
2. 11 + ☐ = 20
3. 1 + ☐ = 12
4. ☐ + 11 = 17
5. 11 + ☐ = 16
6. ☐ + 11 = 14
7. ☐ + 11 = 13
8. 11 + ☐ = 18
9. ☐ + 11 = 16
10. 11 + ☐ = 15
11. 3 + ☐ = 14
12. ☐ + 11 = 17
13. 1 + ☐ = 12
14. ☐ + 11 = 13
15. 4 + ☐ = 15
16. 11 + ☐ = 18
17. ☐ + 11 = 19
18. 2 + ☐ = 13
19. ☐ + 11 = 20
20. 7 + ☐ = 18
21. 11 + ☐ = 19
22. ☐ + 11 = 12
23. ☐ + 11 = 17
24. 5 + ☐ = 16
25. ☐ + 11 = 14

Exercise 29B

26. ☐ + 11 = 13
27. 11 + ☐ = 18
28. ☐ + 11 = 16
29. 9 + ☐ = 20
30. 11 + ☐ = 16
31. ☐ + 11 = 17
32. ☐ + 11 = 14
33. 11 + ☐ = 12
34. ☐ + 11 = 15
35. 11 + ☐ = 11
36. 11 + ☐ = 14
37. ☐ + 11 = 18
38. 11 + ☐ = 16
39. ☐ + 11 = 13
40. 11 + ☐ = 12
41. 11 + ☐ = 17
42. ☐ + 11 = 14
43. 11 + ☐ = 19
44. ☐ + 11 = 15
45. 11 + ☐ = 13
46. 11 + ☐ = 16
47. ☐ + 11 = 20
48. 11 + ☐ = 15
49. ☐ + 11 = 12
50. ☐ + 11 = 17

Exercise 29C

51. ☐ + 3 = 14
52. 11 + ☐ = 18
53. ☐ + 1 = 12
54. ☐ + 11 = 16
55. 9 + ☐ = 20
56. ☐ + 11 = 15
57. 2 + ☐ = 13
58. 11 + ☐ = 15
59. ☐ + 0 = 11
60. 3 + ☐ = 14
61. ☐ + 11 = 16
62. ☐ + 8 = 19
63. 11 + ☐ = 12
64. ☐ + 9 = 20
65. 11 + ☐ = 17
66. ☐ + 1 = 12
67. 11 + ☐ = 15
68. 0 + ☐ = 11
69. ☐ + 11 = 19
70. ☐ + 2 = 13
71. 6 + ☐ = 17
72. ☐ + 11 = 14
73. 11 + ☐ = 13
74. ☐ + 11 = 11
75. 11 + ☐ = 18

Exercise 29D

76. ☐ + 11 = 13
77. 8 + ☐ = 19
78. 0 + ☐ = 11
79. ☐ + 4 = 15
80. 11 + ☐ = 17
81. 2 + ☐ = 13
82. ☐ + 11 = 12
83. 9 + ☐ = 20
84. 3 + ☐ = 14
85. ☐ + 4 = 15
86. 11 + ☐ = 19
87. 0 + ☐ = 11
88. ☐ + 11 = 15
89. 11 + ☐ = 18
90. ☐ + 5 = 16
91. 1 + ☐ = 12
92. ☐ + 11 = 11
93. 3 + ☐ = 14
94. 11 + ☐ = 17
95. ☐ + 9 = 20
96. 1 + ☐ = 12
97. ☐ + 11 = 13
98. 7 + ☐ = 18
99. ☐ + 5 = 16
100. ☐ + 11 = 14

Time? | Time? | Time? | Time?

Try to be even quicker next time!

Can you try to be faster?

Did you do well?

What have you learnt today?

Exercise 30A	Exercise 30B	Exercise 30C	Exercise 30D
Name:	Name:	Name:	Name:
Date:	Date:	Date:	Date:

#	A	#	B	#	C	#	D
1	☐ + 12 = 16	26	12 + ☐ = 17	51	☐ + 12 = 20	76	☐ + 5 = 17
2	12 + ☐ = 15	27	☐ + 2 = 14	52	12 + ☐ = 16	77	12 + ☐ = 20
3	☐ + 8 = 20	28	4 + ☐ = 16	53	☐ + 0 = 12	78	3 + ☐ = 15
4	1 + ☐ = 13	29	☐ + 12 = 12	54	12 + ☐ = 17	79	☐ + 12 = 16
5	☐ + 12 = 17	30	6 + ☐ = 18	55	7 + ☐ = 19	80	☐ + 0 = 12
6	0 + ☐ = 12	31	12 + ☐ = 17	56	☐ + 12 = 15	81	12 + ☐ = 14
7	12 + ☐ = 19	32	☐ + 0 = 12	57	12 + ☐ = 13	82	☐ + 4 = 16
8	☐ + 5 = 17	33	12 + ☐ = 18	58	☐ + 12 = 18	83	12 + ☐ = 19
9	12 + ☐ = 13	34	☐ + 12 = 16	59	12 + ☐ = 20	84	2 + ☐ = 14
10	☐ + 2 = 14	35	☐ + 5 = 17	60	2 + ☐ = 14	85	☐ + 12 = 17
11	12 + ☐ = 18	36	12 + ☐ = 13	61	☐ + 12 = 16	86	☐ + 3 = 15
12	☐ + 3 = 15	37	☐ + 7 = 19	62	5 + ☐ = 17	87	12 + ☐ = 12
13	1 + ☐ = 13	38	12 + ☐ = 15	63	12 + ☐ = 15	88	☐ + 12 = 18
14	☐ + 12 = 16	39	1 + ☐ = 13	64	☐ + 12 = 13	89	4 + ☐ = 16
15	☐ + 6 = 18	40	☐ + 12 = 14	65	12 + ☐ = 18	90	☐ + 12 = 20
16	12 + ☐ = 15	41	☐ + 8 = 20	66	☐ + 12 = 16	91	1 + ☐ = 13
17	☐ + 5 = 17	42	12 + ☐ = 18	67	☐ + 0 = 12	92	12 + ☐ = 18
18	12 + ☐ = 14	43	☐ + 12 = 19	68	12 + ☐ = 14	93	☐ + 1 = 13
19	0 + ☐ = 12	44	3 + ☐ = 15	69	☐ + 12 = 17	94	☐ + 12 = 14
20	☐ + 12 = 19	45	☐ + 12 = 12	70	12 + ☐ = 15	95	0 + ☐ = 12
21	5 + ☐ = 17	46	☐ + 7 = 19	71	☐ + 12 = 13	96	☐ + 5 = 17
22	☐ + 12 = 13	47	12 + ☐ = 14	72	☐ + 12 = 18	97	12 + ☐ = 19
23	☐ + 3 = 15	48	☐ + 12 = 16	73	12 + ☐ = 14	98	☐ + 6 = 18
24	12 + ☐ = 12	49	1 + ☐ = 13	74	☐ + 12 = 12	99	12 + ☐ = 13
25	☐ + 8 = 20	50	☐ + 12 = 20	75	12 + ☐ = 19	100	☐ + 12 = 15

Time?	Time?	Time?	Time?
Did you use strategies?	Where can you improve?	Are you improving?	Did you do well?

Exercise 31A	Exercise 31B	Exercise 31C	Exercise 31D
Name:	Name:	Name:	Name:
Date:	Date:	Date:	Date:

1 $\square + 9 = 13$ **26** $\square + 0 = 9$ **51** $\square + 4 = 13$ **76** $\square + 9 = 12$

2 $9 + \square = 11$ **27** $9 + \square = 17$ **52** $9 + \square = 10$ **77** $0 + \square = 9$

3 $9 + \square = 19$ **28** $4 + \square = 13$ **53** $9 + \square = 18$ **78** $9 + \square = 20$

4 $\square + 9 = 14$ **29** $\square + 9 = 20$ **54** $\square + 5 = 14$ **79** $\square + 4 = 13$

5 $9 + \square = 9$ **30** $9 + \square = 10$ **55** $\square + 9 = 11$ **80** $9 + \square = 10$

6 $\square + 8 = 17$ **31** $\square + 9 = 18$ **56** $10 + \square = 19$ **81** $\square + 5 = 14$

7 $9 + \square = 18$ **32** $\square + 5 = 14$ **57** $\square + 9 = 15$ **82** $\square + 9 = 11$

8 $\square + 9 = 20$ **33** $9 + \square = 9$ **58** $9 + \square = 12$ **83** $7 + \square = 16$

9 $\square + 3 = 12$ **34** $\square + 2 = 11$ **59** $\square + 11 = 20$ **84** $9 + \square = 15$

10 $8 + \square = 17$ **35** $9 + \square = 19$ **60** $9 + \square = 16$ **85** $\square + 3 = 12$

11 $\square + 9 = 10$ **36** $6 + \square = 15$ **61** $9 + \square = 13$ **86** $9 + \square = 18$

12 $5 + \square = 14$ **37** $\square + 9 = 12$ **62** $\square + 9 = 9$ **87** $\square + 7 = 16$

13 $\square + 11 = 20$ **38** $9 + \square = 20$ **63** $\square + 9 = 17$ **88** $9 + \square = 13$

14 $9 + \square = 16$ **39** $9 + \square = 16$ **64** $5 + \square = 14$ **89** $10 + \square = 19$

15 $9 + \square = 12$ **40** $\square + 9 = 13$ **65** $0 + \square = 9$ **90** $\square + 9 = 17$

16 $\square + 9 = 9$ **41** $\square + 9 = 9$ **66** $\square + 9 = 18$ **91** $5 + \square = 14$

17 $9 + \square = 17$ **42** $8 + \square = 17$ **67** $6 + \square = 15$ **92** $\square + 9 = 18$

18 $6 + \square = 15$ **43** $\square + 9 = 14$ **68** $\square + 1 = 10$ **93** $\square + 6 = 15$

19 $\square + 9 = 10$ **44** $1 + \square = 10$ **69** $10 + \square = 19$ **94** $9 + \square = 17$

20 $9 + \square = 16$ **45** $\square + 9 = 18$ **70** $\square + 9 = 16$ **95** $\square + 0 = 9$

21 $\square + 9 = 14$ **46** $9 + \square = 15$ **71** $2 + \square = 11$ **96** $9 + \square = 19$

22 $2 + \square = 11$ **47** $\square + 9 = 11$ **72** $\square + 9 = 20$ **97** $\square + 1 = 10$

23 $9 + \square = 15$ **48** $\square + 10 = 19$ **73** $\square + 8 = 17$ **98** $9 + \square = 16$

24 $\square + 3 = 12$ **49** $9 + \square = 16$ **74** $9 + \square = 12$ **99** $11 + \square = 20$

25 $\square + 9 = 13$ **50** $9 + \square = 12$ **75** $\square + 0 = 9$ **100** $\square + 9 = 11$

Time?	Time?	Time?	Time?

Which facts did you find the hardest?

Did you beat your target?

Can you try to be faster?

Where do you need to improve?

Exercise 32A	Exercise 32B	Exercise 32C	Exercise 32D
Name:	Name:	Name:	Name:
Date:	Date:	Date:	Date:

1 ☐ + 7 = 14	**26** ☐ + 3 = 6	**51** ☐ + 9 = 19	**76** ☐ + 8 = 17
2 3 + ☐ = 7	**27** 10 + ☐ = 20	**52** 1 + ☐ = 2	**77** ☐ + 4 = 8
3 ☐ + 6 = 11	**28** ☐ + 1 = 3	**53** 3 + ☐ = 5	**78** 3 + ☐ = 5
4 5 + ☐ = 10	**29** 9 + ☐ = 18	**54** ☐ + 10 = 20	**79** 10 + ☐ = 20
5 ☐ + 7 = 15	**30** 4 + ☐ = 7	**55** 3 + ☐ = 7	**80** ☐ + 4 = 7
6 8 + ☐ = 16	**31** ☐ + 5 = 9	**56** ☐ + 2 = 4	**81** 3 + ☐ = 6
7 ☐ + 8 = 17	**32** 4 + ☐ = 8	**57** ☐ + 8 = 17	**82** ☐ + 9 = 19
8 5 + ☐ = 9	**33** ☐ + 6 = 13	**58** 2 + ☐ = 3	**83** 9 + ☐ = 18
9 ☐ + 1 = 2	**34** ☐ + 8 = 16	**59** ☐ + 7 = 15	**84** ☐ + 5 = 9
10 ☐ + 3 = 7	**35** 3 + ☐ = 7	**60** 6 + ☐ = 12	**85** ☐ + 6 = 11
11 6 + ☐ = 11	**36** ☐ + 8 = 15	**61** ☐ + 8 = 15	**86** 1 + ☐ = 2
12 6 + ☐ = 12	**37** 2 + ☐ = 4	**62** 8 + ☐ = 16	**87** ☐ + 7 = 13
13 ☐ + 2 = 3	**38** ☐ + 3 = 5	**63** 4 + ☐ = 7	**88** 8 + ☐ = 16
14 9 + ☐ = 18	**39** 9 + ☐ = 17	**64** ☐ + 5 = 9	**89** ☐ + 2 = 3
15 ☐ + 10 = 19	**40** 5 + ☐ = 10	**65** ☐ + 10 = 19	**90** ☐ + 2 = 4
16 3 + ☐ = 6	**41** ☐ + 3 = 7	**66** 4 + ☐ = 8	**91** 7 + ☐ = 15
17 5 + ☐ = 11	**42** ☐ + 7 = 14	**67** ☐ + 7 = 14	**92** 6 + ☐ = 11
18 ☐ + 4 = 9	**43** 5 + ☐ = 9	**68** 6 + ☐ = 13	**93** ☐ + 5 = 10
19 4 + ☐ = 7	**44** ☐ + 10 = 19	**69** 9 + ☐ = 18	**94** 8 + ☐ = 17
20 ☐ + 9 = 17	**45** 6 + ☐ = 11	**70** ☐ + 6 = 11	**95** ☐ + 7 = 14
21 ☐ + 10 = 20	**46** ☐ + 4 = 7	**71** 9 + ☐ = 17	**96** 4 + ☐ = 9
22 3 + ☐ = 5	**47** 6 + ☐ = 12	**72** ☐ + 3 = 6	**97** ☐ + 2 = 5
23 ☐ + 2 = 4	**48** ☐ + 6 = 13	**73** ☐ + 4 = 9	**98** ☐ + 6 = 13
24 ☐ + 2 = 3	**49** 7 + ☐ = 15	**74** 2 + ☐ = 5	**99** 8 + ☐ = 15
25 4 + ☐ = 8	**50** 1 + ☐ = 2	**75** ☐ + 5 = 10	**100** ☐ + 6 = 12

Time?	Time?	Time?	Time?
Is this your best score?	Have you reached your target?	Did you do well?	Do you think you are improving?

Exercise 33A	Exercise 33B	Exercise 33C	Exercise 33D
Name:	Name:	Name:	Name:
Date:	Date:	Date:	Date:

Exercise 33A

1. $13 + \square = 17$
2. $13 + \square = 16$
3. $\square + 5 = 20$
4. $11 + \square = 13$
5. $\square + 4 = 17$
6. $12 + \square = 14$
7. $\square + 12 = 15$
8. $1 + \square = 12$
9. $4 + \square = 18$
10. $\square + 12 = 14$
11. $12 + \square = 15$
12. $\square + 3 = 16$
13. $1 + \square = 12$
14. $\square + 3 = 17$
15. $3 + \square = 16$
16. $12 + \square = 13$
17. $\square + 4 = 17$
18. $5 + \square = 20$
19. $\square + 5 = 19$
20. $13 + \square = 15$
21. $2 + \square = 14$
22. $\square + 13 = 16$
23. $14 + \square = 19$
24. $12 + \square = 15$
25. $\square + 4 = 19$

Exercise 33B

26. $\square + 14 = 18$
27. $2 + \square = 14$
28. $12 + \square = 15$
29. $\square + 14 = 17$
30. $1 + \square = 12$
31. $2 + \square = 15$
32. $\square + 15 = 19$
33. $3 + \square = 16$
34. $13 + \square = 17$
35. $\square + 14 = 18$
36. $14 + \square = 17$
37. $5 + \square = 20$
38. $\square + 13 = 15$
39. $12 + \square = 14$
40. $\square + 13 = 17$
41. $5 + \square = 19$
42. $\square + 3 = 15$
43. $1 + \square = 12$
44. $14 + \square = 18$
45. $\square + 15 = 20$
46. $3 + \square = 15$
47. $\square + 13 = 16$
48. $\square + 1 = 13$
49. $14 + \square = 18$
50. $\square + 11 = 12$

Exercise 33C

51. $\square + 12 = 14$
52. $13 + \square = 15$
53. $\square + 11 = 12$
54. $\square + 5 = 19$
55. $5 + \square = 20$
56. $11 + \square = 12$
57. $\square + 2 = 13$
58. $12 + \square = 15$
59. $3 + \square = 17$
60. $\square + 3 = 15$
61. $5 + \square = 20$
62. $\square + 12 = 14$
63. $3 + \square = 16$
64. $\square + 1 = 12$
65. $12 + \square = 15$
66. $\square + 4 = 17$
67. $3 + \square = 16$
68. $2 + \square = 13$
69. $\square + 4 = 19$
70. $12 + \square = 15$
71. $\square + 4 = 17$
72. $11 + \square = 13$
73. $4 + \square = 18$
74. $\square + 15 = 19$
75. $2 + \square = 14$

Exercise 33D

76. $\square + 1 = 13$
77. $14 + \square = 18$
78. $3 + \square = 17$
79. $\square + 12 = 15$
80. $\square + 15 = 20$
81. $15 + \square = 19$
82. $3 + \square = 16$
83. $\square + 12 = 14$
84. $11 + \square = 12$
85. $3 + \square = 15$
86. $\square + 13 = 17$
87. $\square + 12 = 14$
88. $5 + \square = 19$
89. $15 + \square = 20$
90. $\square + 13 = 16$
91. $11 + \square = 12$
92. $\square + 14 = 18$
93. $13 + \square = 17$
94. $2 + \square = 15$
95. $\square + 12 = 14$
96. $13 + \square = 16$
97. $2 + \square = 13$
98. $\square + 5 = 20$
99. $3 + \square = 17$
100. $\square + 11 = 13$

Time? | Time? | Time? | Time?

Try to concentrate even more!

How do you think you are doing?

What have you learnt today?

How could you recall these facts even quicker?

Exercise 34A	Exercise 34B	Exercise 34C	Exercise 34D
Name:	Name:	Name:	Name:
Date:	Date:	Date:	Date:

Exercise 34A

1. $7 + \square = 11$
2. $\square + 5 = 18$
3. $3 + \square = 19$
4. $8 + \square = 12$
5. $\square + 6 = 19$
6. $5 + \square = 13$
7. $\square + 6 = 14$
8. $8 + \square = 11$
9. $\square + 5 = 8$
10. $\square + 5 = 13$
11. $6 + \square = 14$
12. $3 + \square = 18$
13. $\square + 8 = 12$
14. $3 + \square = 8$
15. $\square + 7 = 12$
16. $3 + \square = 18$
17. $\square + 4 = 12$
18. $7 + \square = 11$
19. $5 + \square = 13$
20. $\square + 7 = 11$
21. $6 + \square = 14$
22. $5 + \square = 13$
23. $\square + 6 = 14$
24. $7 + \square = 12$
25. $\square + 5 = 18$

Exercise 34B

26. $\square + 5 = 8$
27. $8 + \square = 13$
28. $7 + \square = 11$
29. $\square + 8 = 11$
30. $5 + \square = 12$
31. $3 + \square = 9$
32. $\square + 5 = 12$
33. $3 + \square = 8$
34. $8 + \square = 13$
35. $\square + 8 = 14$
36. $3 + \square = 9$
37. $7 + \square = 11$
38. $\square + 8 = 13$
39. $3 + \square = 18$
40. $8 + \square = 14$
41. $\square + 7 = 12$
42. $3 + \square = 11$
43. $\square + 5 = 18$
44. $\square + 8 = 14$
45. $3 + \square = 8$
46. $\square + 6 = 14$
47. $7 + \square = 12$
48. $\square + 3 = 9$
49. $3 + \square = 18$
50. $\square + 5 = 8$

Exercise 34C

51. $\square + 8 = 12$
52. $13 + \square = 18$
53. $6 + \square = 14$
54. $\square + 5 = 8$
55. $\square + 3 = 11$
56. $15 + \square = 18$
57. $6 + \square = 19$
58. $\square + 8 = 12$
59. $\square + 16 = 19$
60. $5 + \square = 8$
61. $4 + \square = 11$
62. $\square + 6 = 12$
63. $\square + 7 = 13$
64. $3 + \square = 11$
65. $7 + \square = 13$
66. $\square + 3 = 9$
67. $4 + \square = 12$
68. $\square + 6 = 9$
69. $13 + \square = 18$
70. $\square + 5 = 13$
71. $\square + 7 = 11$
72. $3 + \square = 8$
73. $13 + \square = 18$
74. $\square + 7 = 12$
75. $8 + \square = 12$

Exercise 34D

76. $\square + 5 = 12$
77. $3 + \square = 18$
78. $3 + \square = 8$
79. $\square + 5 = 13$
80. $7 + \square = 11$
81. $3 + \square = 11$
82. $\square + 7 = 12$
83. $\square + 6 = 9$
84. $7 + \square = 12$
85. $\square + 6 = 9$
86. $\square + 8 = 13$
87. $7 + \square = 11$
88. $3 + \square = 8$
89. $\square + 5 = 13$
90. $\square + 8 = 14$
91. $3 + \square = 9$
92. $7 + \square = 11$
93. $\square + 8 = 13$
94. $13 + \square = 18$
95. $\square + 6 = 14$
96. $5 + \square = 12$
97. $3 + \square = 9$
98. $\square + 8 = 14$
99. $3 + \square = 8$
100. $\square + 5 = 18$

Time?	Time?	Time?	Time?

Are the facts at your fingertips?   Try to really focus!   Which facts do you find the easiest?   Did you do well?

Exercise 35A	Exercise 35B	Exercise 35C	Exercise 35D
Name:	Name:	Name:	Name:
Date:	Date:	Date:	Date:

1 $1 + \square = 10$	**26** $\square + 10 = 16$	**51** $\square + 17 = 18$	**76** $\square + 1 = 15$
2 $\square + 10 = 17$	**27** $1 + \square = 6$	**52** $7 + \square = 17$	**77** $0 + \square = 16$
3 $10 + \square = 15$	**28** $\square + 0 = 12$	**53** $0 + \square = 16$	**78** $14 + \square = 15$
4 $\square + 1 = 7$	**29** $\square + 4 = 14$	**54** $\square + 10 = 19$	**79** $\square + 9 = 19$
5 $0 + \square = 5$	**30** $13 + \square = 14$	**55** $\square + 11 = 11$	**80** $\square + 0 = 6$
6 $4 + \square = 14$	**31** $\square + 3 = 3$	**56** $19 + \square = 20$	**81** $5 + \square = 6$
7 $\square + 4 = 5$	**32** $2 + \square = 12$	**57** $1 + \square = 13$	**82** $2 + \square = 12$
8 $\square + 0 = 3$	**33** $1 + \square = 2$	**58** $\square + 0 = 20$	**83** $\square + 10 = 16$
9 $10 + \square = 12$	**34** $\square + 0 = 18$	**59** $10 + \square = 18$	**84** $1 + \square = 7$
10 $\square + 10 = 11$	**35** $10 + \square = 19$	**60** $\square + 1 = 15$	**85** $\square + 3 = 3$
11 $0 + \square = 13$	**36** $14 + \square = 15$	**61** $10 + \square = 16$	**86** $\square + 1 = 10$
12 $1 + \square = 7$	**37** $\square + 16 = 16$	**62** $\square + 1 = 17$	**87** $10 + \square = 14$
13 $\square + 1 = 11$	**38** $\square + 10 = 17$	**63** $16 + \square = 16$	**88** $\square + 3 = 13$
14 $\square + 10 = 14$	**39** $1 + \square = 16$	**64** $1 + \square = 5$	**89** $\square + 1 = 11$
15 $0 + \square = 19$	**40** $\square + 14 = 15$	**65** $\square + 3 = 13$	**90** $8 + \square = 9$
16 $\square + 2 = 12$	**41** $\square + 0 = 16$	**66** $\square + 17 = 17$	**91** $\square + 10 = 17$
17 $10 + \square = 16$	**42** $10 + \square = 15$	**67** $3 + \square = 4$	**92** $4 + \square = 4$
18 $13 + \square = 14$	**43** $6 + \square = 7$	**68** $10 + \square = 16$	**93** $\square + 2 = 2$
19 $\square + 9 = 10$	**44** $\square + 17 = 17$	**69** $\square + 1 = 19$	**94** $10 + \square = 13$
20 $\square + 20 = 20$	**45** $3 + \square = 13$	**70** $0 + \square = 2$	**95** $3 + \square = 3$
21 $10 + \square = 20$	**46** $\square + 18 = 19$	**71** $\square + 4 = 14$	**96** $\square + 1 = 4$
22 $\square + 2 = 12$	**47** $0 + \square = 8$	**72** $\square + 13 = 14$	**97** $8 + \square = 8$
23 $11 + \square = 11$	**48** $9 + \square = 10$	**73** $12 + \square = 12$	**98** $\square + 3 = 13$
24 $\square + 12 = 13$	**49** $\square + 16 = 16$	**74** $1 + \square = 6$	**99** $9 + \square = 10$
25 $3 + \square = 13$	**50** $\square + 10 = 20$	**75** $\square + 10 = 16$	**100** $\square + 6 = 7$

Time?	Time?	Time?	Time?

Try to be even quicker next time!

Can you try to be faster?

Did you do well?

What have you learnt today?

Exercise 36A	Exercise 36B	Exercise 36C	Exercise 36D
Name:	Name:	Name:	Name:
Date:	Date:	Date:	Date:

1 ☐ + 9 = 11	**26** ☐ + 2 = 6	**51** 17 + ☐ = 18	**76** ☐ + 2 = 6
2 4 + ☐ = 14	**27** 2 + ☐ = 10	**52** ☐ + 3 = 3	**77** 10 + ☐ = 19
3 1 + ☐ = 8	**28** 10 + ☐ = 19	**53** 16 + ☐ = 18	**78** 3 + ☐ = 4
4 ☐ + 0 = 16	**29** ☐ + 1 = 4	**54** ☐ + 8 = 18	**79** ☐ + 0 = 1
5 2 + ☐ = 11	**30** 1 + ☐ = 1	**55** 5 + ☐ = 6	**80** 2 + ☐ = 12
6 4 + ☐ = 5	**31** ☐ + 15 = 17	**56** 0 + ☐ = 15	**81** 1 + ☐ = 15
7 ☐ + 0 = 17	**32** ☐ + 10 = 12	**57** ☐ + 2 = 16	**82** ☐ + 2 = 16
8 2 + ☐ = 8	**33** 1 + ☐ = 15	**58** 10 + ☐ = 12	**83** 10 + ☐ = 19
9 3 + ☐ = 5	**34** ☐ + 2 = 16	**59** ☐ + 1 = 8	**84** 7 + ☐ = 8
10 ☐ + 10 = 13	**35** 10 + ☐ = 19	**60** 9 + ☐ = 9	**85** ☐ + 9 = 9
11 ☐ + 1 = 19	**36** 7 + ☐ = 8	**61** 2 + ☐ = 15	**86** 2 + ☐ = 15
12 0 + ☐ = 2	**37** ☐ + 0 = 9	**62** ☐ + 10 = 14	**87** 5 + ☐ = 15
13 2 + ☐ = 6	**38** 2 + ☐ = 15	**63** 1 + ☐ = 3	**88** ☐ + 2 = 3
14 ☐ + 10 = 12	**39** ☐ + 2 = 16	**64** 10 + ☐ = 10	**89** ☐ + 0 = 10
15 ☐ + 5 = 6	**40** ☐ + 9 = 19	**65** ☐ + 12 = 14	**90** 2 + ☐ = 14
16 0 + ☐ = 3	**41** 7 + ☐ = 8	**66** 4 + ☐ = 6	**91** 4 + ☐ = 5
17 ☐ + 2 = 3	**42** ☐ + 0 = 9	**67** ☐ + 11 = 12	**92** ☐ + 11 = 12
18 10 + ☐ = 11	**43** 2 + ☐ = 15	**68** 0 + ☐ = 3	**93** 3 + ☐ = 3
19 ☐ + 2 = 9	**44** 5 + ☐ = 15	**69** 2 + ☐ = 20	**94** ☐ + 15 = 17
20 10 + ☐ = 16	**45** ☐ + 2 = 3	**70** ☐ + 10 = 18	**95** 6 + ☐ = 16
21 ☐ + 1 = 7	**46** 10 + ☐ = 10	**71** 5 + ☐ = 6	**96** 13 + ☐ = 15
22 0 + ☐ = 16	**47** ☐ + 12 = 14	**72** 7 + ☐ = 9	**97** ☐ + 11 = 13
23 ☐ + 10 = 17	**48** 4 + ☐ = 14	**73** ☐ + 6 = 16	**98** ☐ + 7 = 17
24 1 + ☐ = 9	**49** ☐ + 11 = 12	**74** 0 + ☐ = 12	**99** 6 + ☐ = 6
25 ☐ + 13 = 13	**50** 3 + ☐ = 3	**75** ☐ + 2 = 7	**100** 3 + ☐ = 5

Time?	Time?	Time?	Time?
Did you use strategies?	Where can you improve?	Are you improving?	Did you do well?

Exercise 37A	Exercise 37B	Exercise 37C	Exercise 37D
Name:	Name:	Name:	Name:
Date:	Date:	Date:	Date:

1. ☐ + 16 = 17
2. 20 + ☐ = 20
3. ☐ + 10 = 16
4. ☐ + 2 = 7
5. 11 + ☐ = 15
6. ☐ + 17 = 18
7. 0 + ☐ = 19
8. 3 + ☐ = 13
9. ☐ + 5 = 16
10. 9 + ☐ = 11
11. ☐ + 8 = 19
12. 7 + ☐ = 9
13. ☐ + 6 = 16
14. ☐ + 14 = 14
15. 18 + ☐ = 19
16. ☐ + 19 = 20
17. 7 + ☐ = 18
18. ☐ + 13 = 13
19. 2 + ☐ = 13
20. 6 + ☐ = 16
21. ☐ + 5 = 16
22. ☐ + 18 = 19
23. 4 + ☐ = 4
24. ☐ + 10 = 10
25. ☐ + 14 = 16

26. 9 + ☐ = 20
27. ☐ + 7 = 17
28. 12 + ☐ = 12
29. 9 + ☐ = 10
30. ☐ + 6 = 17
31. 3 + ☐ = 5
32. ☐ + 15 = 15
33. ☐ + 5 = 6
34. 4 + ☐ = 14
35. 11 + ☐ = 14
36. ☐ + 16 = 18
37. 18 + ☐ = 18
38. ☐ + 17 = 19
39. 6 + ☐ = 16
40. ☐ + 11 = 19
41. ☐ + 7 = 17
42. 14 + ☐ = 16
43. 19 + ☐ = 20
44. ☐ + 11 = 18
45. ☐ + 8 = 10
46. 2 + ☐ = 20
47. ☐ + 9 = 20
48. 8 + ☐ = 18
49. ☐ + 6 = 17
50. 0 + ☐ = 10

51. ☐ + 13 = 14
52. 6 + ☐ = 17
53. 2 + ☐ = 16
54. ☐ + 11 = 20
55. ☐ + 19 = 19
56. 10 + ☐ = 14
57. ☐ + 15 = 17
58. 7 + ☐ = 17
59. ☐ + 12 = 13
60. 6 + ☐ = 16
61. ☐ + 2 = 17
62. 8 + ☐ = 8
63. ☐ + 10 = 19
64. 7 + ☐ = 18
65. ☐ + 16 = 18
66. 1 + ☐ = 19
67. ☐ + 8 = 19
68. ☐ + 17 = 18
69. 4 + ☐ = 15
70. ☐ + 14 = 14
71. 10 + ☐ = 17
72. ☐ + 18 = 20
73. 6 + ☐ = 17
74. ☐ + 17 = 19
75. 3 + ☐ = 5

76. ☐ + 2 = 13
77. 4 + ☐ = 14
78. ☐ + 2 = 4
79. 3 + ☐ = 14
80. ☐ + 8 = 19
81. ☐ + 10 = 13
82. 5 + ☐ = 16
83. 6 + ☐ = 8
84. ☐ + 6 = 8
85. 5 + ☐ = 15
86. ☐ + 10 = 20
87. 14 + ☐ = 14
88. 7 + ☐ = 9
89. ☐ + 3 = 4
90. ☐ + 6 = 17
91. 6 + ☐ = 16
92. ☐ + 18 = 19
93. 10 + ☐ = 12
94. ☐ + 5 = 6
95. 7 + ☐ = 17
96. 1 + ☐ = 3
97. ☐ + 8 = 9
98. 9 + ☐ = 19
99. ☐ + 4 = 15
100. ☐ + 7 = 17

Time?	Time?	Time?	Time?

How did you do? Did you beat your best score? Can you try to be faster? Have you reached your target?

Exercise 38A	Exercise 38B	Exercise 38C	Exercise 38D
Name:	Name:	Name:	Name:
Date:	Date:	Date:	Date:

Exercise 38A

1. $\square + 2 = 12$
2. $6 + \square = 18$
3. $4 + \square = 14$
4. $\square + 6 = 7$
5. $4 + \square = 15$
6. $\square + 4 = 6$
7. $3 + \square = 15$
8. $\square + 6 = 16$
9. $5 + \square = 6$
10. $\square + 3 = 14$
11. $13 + \square = 13$
12. $\square + 7 = 9$
13. $\square + 2 = 14$
14. $8 + \square = 18$
15. $\square + 14 = 15$
16. $5 + \square = 16$
17. $\square + 14 = 16$
18. $7 + \square = 19$
19. $5 + \square = 15$
20. $\square + 3 = 4$
21. $6 + \square = 17$
22. $\square + 18 = 20$
23. $\square + 1 = 13$
24. $7 + \square = 17$
25. $\square + 9 = 10$

Exercise 38B

26. $\square + 0 = 5$
27. $\square + 16 = 16$
28. $11 + \square = 13$
29. $\square + 7 = 19$
30. $8 + \square = 18$
31. $\square + 0 = 11$
32. $\square + 16 = 18$
33. $15 + \square = 17$
34. $6 + \square = 18$
35. $\square + 1 = 11$
36. $1 + \square = 12$
37. $\square + 19 = 19$
38. $5 + \square = 7$
39. $\square + 4 = 16$
40. $4 + \square = 14$
41. $2 + \square = 13$
42. $\square + 0 = 20$
43. $12 + \square = 13$
44. $\square + 13 = 15$
45. $12 + \square = 17$
46. $\square + 2 = 12$
47. $3 + \square = 14$
48. $\square + 6 = 6$
49. $9 + \square = 11$
50. $\square + 3 = 15$

Exercise 38C

51. $\square + 6 = 16$
52. $\square + 11 = 15$
53. $12 + \square = 12$
54. $17 + \square = 19$
55. $\square + 2 = 14$
56. $8 + \square = 18$
57. $\square + 6 = 17$
58. $0 + \square = 18$
59. $\square + 1 = 3$
60. $\square + 1 = 13$
61. $9 + \square = 19$
62. $\square + 1 = 15$
63. $8 + \square = 19$
64. $\square + 6 = 8$
65. $0 + \square = 12$
66. $3 + \square = 13$
67. $\square + 1 = 12$
68. $11 + \square = 14$
69. $\square + 3 = 5$
70. $9 + \square = 11$
71. $10 + \square = 15$
72. $\square + 1 = 14$
73. $11 + \square = 19$
74. $\square + 12 = 14$
75. $12 + \square = 16$

Exercise 38D

76. $\square + 5 = 17$
77. $3 + \square = 13$
78. $\square + 7 = 18$
79. $2 + \square = 12$
80. $\square + 8 = 10$
81. $12 + \square = 18$
82. $\square + 0 = 9$
83. $12 + \square = 14$
84. $\square + 16 = 16$
85. $6 + \square = 8$
86. $\square + 8 = 20$
87. $7 + \square = 17$
88. $\square + 19 = 20$
89. $\square + 10 = 10$
90. $15 + \square = 17$
91. $2 + \square = 13$
92. $\square + 10 = 16$
93. $11 + \square = 18$
94. $\square + 16 = 17$
95. $18 + \square = 20$
96. $\square + 12 = 15$
97. $10 + \square = 14$
98. $\square + 11 = 20$
99. $13 + \square = 13$
100. $\square + 12 = 19$

Time? | Time? | Time? | Time?

How do you think you are doing?

How did you do?

Is this your best score?

Which facts do you find the easiest?

Exercise 39A	**Exercise 39B**	**Exercise 39C**	**Exercise 39D**
Name:	Name:	Name:	Name:
Date:	Date:	Date:	Date:

1 $18 + \square = 18$　**26** $12 + \square = 17$　**51** $\square + 12 = 20$　**76** $6 + \square = 16$

2 $\square + 1 = 7$　**27** $\square + 10 = 16$　**52** $9 + \square = 19$　**77** $\square + 5 = 17$

3 $9 + \square = 13$　**28** $8 + \square = 19$　**53** $\square + 11 = 17$　**78** $4 + \square = 13$

4 $12 + \square = 18$　**29** $\square + 9 = 11$　**54** $10 + \square = 18$　**79** $\square + 5 = 16$

5 $\square + 11 = 18$　**30** $10 + \square = 20$　**55** $6 + \square = 7$　**80** $9 + \square = 10$

6 $17 + \square = 19$　**31** $\square + 0 = 3$　**56** $\square + 4 = 13$　**81** $\square + 0 = 3$

7 $\square + 10 = 13$　**32** $9 + \square = 10$　**57** $12 + \square = 18$　**82** $10 + \square = 10$

8 $\square + 19 = 19$　**33** $\square + 5 = 16$　**58** $\square + 11 = 16$　**83** $\square + 9 = 11$

9 $1 + \square = 17$　**34** $4 + \square = 13$　**59** $17 + \square = 19$　**84** $8 + \square = 19$

10 $\square + 9 = 12$　**35** $\square + 5 = 17$　**60** $3 + \square = 13$　**85** $12 + \square = 17$

11 $2 + \square = 14$　**36** $6 + \square = 16$　**61** $\square + 19 = 19$　**86** $\square + 9 = 13$

12 $\square + 7 = 18$　**37** $2 + \square = 5$　**62** $1 + \square = 17$　**87** $1 + \square = 8$

13 $15 + \square = 17$　**38** $\square + 6 = 15$　**63** $\square + 9 = 12$　**88** $\square + 4 = 4$

14 $10 + \square = 18$　**39** $7 + \square = 18$　**64** $2 + \square = 14$　**89** $6 + \square = 16$

15 $\square + 0 = 13$　**40** $5 + \square = 17$　**65** $\square + 7 = 18$　**90** $\square + 6 = 17$

16 $1 + \square = 15$　**41** $\square + 8 = 10$　**66** $15 + \square = 17$　**91** $5 + \square = 16$

17 $\square + 9 = 11$　**42** $7 + \square = 17$　**67** $10 + \square = 18$　**92** $2 + \square = 10$

18 $11 + \square = 17$　**43** $\square + 0 = 11$　**68** $\square + 0 = 13$　**93** $\square + 10 = 17$

19 $\square + 12 = 13$　**44** $1 + \square = 7$　**69** $1 + \square = 15$　**94** $11 + \square = 11$

20 $10 + \square = 13$　**45** $\square + 12 = 20$　**70** $\square + 9 = 11$　**95** $1 + \square = 7$

21 $\square + 1 = 10$　**46** $9 + \square = 16$　**71** $11 + \square = 17$　**96** $\square + 7 = 16$

22 $11 + \square = 5$　**47** $9 + \square = 20$　**72** $\square + 12 = 13$　**97** $9 + \square = 20$

23 $4 + \square = 13$　**48** $\square + 10 = 20$　**73** $10 + \square = 13$　**98** $\square + 10 = 14$

24 $\square + 5 = 16$　**49** $16 + \square = 16$　**74** $\square + 6 = 15$　**99** $16 + \square = 16$

25 $4 + \square = 15$　**50** $\square + 13 = 14$　**75** $2 + \square = 5$　**100** $\square + 13 = 14$

Time?	Time?	Time?	Time?

Did you do well?　What have you learnt today?　Have you reached your target?　What is your time?

Exercise 40A	Exercise 40B	Exercise 40C	Exercise 40D
Name:	Name:	Name:	Name:
Date:	Date:	Date:	Date:

Exercise 40A

1. $6 + \square = 16$
2. $\square + 6 = 17$
3. $5 + \square = 14$
4. $2 + \square = 10$
5. $\square + 10 = 17$
6. $13 + \square = 13$
7. $\square + 7 = 14$
8. $\square + 1 = 15$
9. $9 + \square = 11$
10. $\square + 12 = 13$
11. $10 + \square = 13$
12. $\square + 6 = 15$
13. $8 + \square = 10$
14. $7 + \square = 17$
15. $\square + 0 = 11$
16. $8 + \square = 16$
17. $\square + 6 = 7$
18. $12 + \square = 20$
19. $\square + 9 = 16$
20. $9 + \square = 20$
21. $\square + 10 = 20$
22. $9 + \square = 18$
23. $16 + \square = 16$
24. $\square + 13 = 14$
25. $10 + \square = 14$

Exercise 40B

26. $9 + \square = 20$
27. $\square + 0 = 3$
28. $6 + \square = 12$
29. $\square + 9 = 10$
30. $5 + \square = 16$
31. $\square + 4 = 13$
32. $5 + \square = 17$
33. $\square + 6 = 16$
34. $11 + \square = 17$
35. $\square + 10 = 18$
36. $4 + \square = 8$
37. $6 + \square = 7$
38. $\square + 4 = 13$
39. $12 + \square = 18$
40. $11 + \square = 16$
41. $\square + 17 = 19$
42. $3 + \square = 13$
43. $\square + 19 = 19$
44. $9 + \square = 18$
45. $\square + 1 = 17$
46. $9 + \square = 12$
47. $2 + \square = 14$
48. $\square + 7 = 18$
49. $15 + \square = 17$
50. $\square + 10 = 18$

Exercise 40C

51. $\square + 10 = 20$
52. $9 + \square = 20$
53. $\square + 9 = 16$
54. $12 + \square = 20$
55. $1 + \square = 7$
56. $\square + 0 = 11$
57. $7 + \square = 17$
58. $\square + 2 = 4$
59. $8 + \square = 10$
60. $5 + \square = 17$
61. $\square + 7 = 18$
62. $6 + \square = 15$
63. $\square + 2 = 5$
64. $6 + \square = 16$
65. $\square + 7 = 14$
66. $5 + \square = 17$
67. $4 + \square = 13$
68. $\square + 5 = 16$
69. $9 + \square = 10$
70. $\square + 0 = 3$
71. $10 + \square = 20$
72. $\square + 8 = 16$
73. $9 + \square = 11$
74. $\square + 8 = 19$
75. $10 + \square = 16$

Exercise 40D

76. $1 + \square = 18$
77. $\square + 9 = 12$
78. $2 + \square = 14$
79. $\square + 7 = 14$
80. $7 + \square = 18$
81. $\square + 15 = 17$
82. $10 + \square = 18$
83. $\square + 7 = 14$
84. $1 + \square = 15$
85. $9 + \square = 11$
86. $\square + 3 = 6$
87. $11 + \square = 17$
88. $\square + 10 = 13$
89. $16 + \square = 16$
90. $\square + 2 = 5$
91. $6 + \square = 15$
92. $7 + \square = 18$
93. $\square + 2 = 14$
94. $6 + \square = 12$
95. $15 + \square = 17$
96. $\square + 0 = 13$
97. $1 + \square = 15$
98. $\square + 9 = 11$
99. $11 + \square = 17$
100. $\square + 6 = 15$

Time? | Time? | Time? | Time?

Try to be even quicker next time?

How are you doing?

Try to be faster?

Did you beat your target?

Exercise 41A	Exercise 41B	Exercise 41C	Exercise 41D
Name:	Name:	Name:	Name:
Date:	Date:	Date:	Date:

	Exercise 41A		Exercise 41B		Exercise 41C		Exercise 41D
1	$\square + 9 = 17$	**26**	$\square + 7 = 18$	**51**	$\square + 9 = 16$	**76**	$\square + 2 = 19$
2	$7 + \square = 18$	**27**	$4 + \square = 16$	**52**	$16 + \square = 17$	**77**	$\square + 8 = 18$
3	$2 + \square = 19$	**28**	$\square + 8 = 18$	**53**	$6 + \square = 12$	**78**	$11 + \square = 15$
4	$\square + 0 = 15$	**29**	$7 + \square = 15$	**54**	$\square + 1 = 19$	**79**	$\square + 9 = 16$
5	$1 + \square = 9$	**30**	$10 + \square = 18$	**55**	$9 + \square = 18$	**80**	$16 + \square = 17$
6	$\square + 5 = 11$	**31**	$\square + 2 = 19$	**56**	$\square + 3 = 5$	**81**	$\square + 12 = 18$
7	$9 + \square = 19$	**32**	$9 + \square = 15$	**57**	$7 + \square = 16$	**82**	$18 + \square = 19$
8	$\square + 4 = 8$	**33**	$\square + 3 = 15$	**58**	$\square + 1 = 20$	**83**	$\square + 9 = 18$
9	$\square + 3 = 15$	**34**	$6 + \square = 12$	**59**	$6 + \square = 17$	**84**	$2 + \square = 5$
10	$6 + \square = 17$	**35**	$\square + 3 = 7$	**60**	$\square + 8 = 15$	**85**	$7 + \square = 16$
11	$9 + \square = 14$	**36**	$\square + 11 = 13$	**61**	$2 + \square = 19$	**86**	$\square + 1 = 20$
12	$\square + 2 = 15$	**37**	$10 + \square = 18$	**62**	$15 + \square = 15$	**87**	$6 + \square = 17$
13	$3 + \square = 7$	**38**	$\square + 2 = 8$	**63**	$\square + 8 = 9$	**88**	$\square + 8 = 15$
14	$\square + 9 = 18$	**39**	$9 + \square = 17$	**64**	$6 + \square = 11$	**89**	$3 + \square = 12$
15	$9 + \square = 15$	**40**	$5 + \square = 7$	**65**	$\square + 10 = 19$	**90**	$\square + 8 = 18$
16	$\square + 2 = 16$	**41**	$6 + \square = 11$	**66**	$4 + \square = 8$	**91**	$6 + \square = 17$
17	$3 + \square = 15$	**42**	$\square + 7 = 18$	**67**	$\square + 3 = 15$	**92**	$\square + 9 = 11$
18	$\square + 6 = 8$	**43**	$\square + 12 = 14$	**68**	$\square + 11 = 17$	**93**	$3 + \square = 7$
19	$5 + \square = 14$	**44**	$10 + \square = 13$	**69**	$\square + 5 = 14$	**94**	$11 + \square = 17$
20	$10 + \square = 20$	**45**	$\square + 10 = 19$	**70**	$13 + \square = 15$	**95**	$\square + 10 = 16$
21	$\square + 7 = 15$	**46**	$4 + \square = 7$	**71**	$\square + 4 = 7$	**96**	$\square + 12 = 14$
22	$6 + \square = 10$	**47**	$\square + 5 = 10$	**72**	$9 + \square = 18$	**97**	$12 + \square = 17$
23	$\square + 12 = 14$	**48**	$\square + 9 = 11$	**73**	$\square + 12 = 16$	**98**	$\square + 9 = 14$
24	$12 + \square = 17$	**49**	$5 + \square = 15$	**74**	$8 + \square = 15$	**99**	$10 + \square = 18$
25	$\square + 9 = 14$	**50**	$\square + 4 = 13$	**75**	$\square + 8 = 18$	**100**	$\square + 6 = 15$

Time?	Time?	Time?	Time?

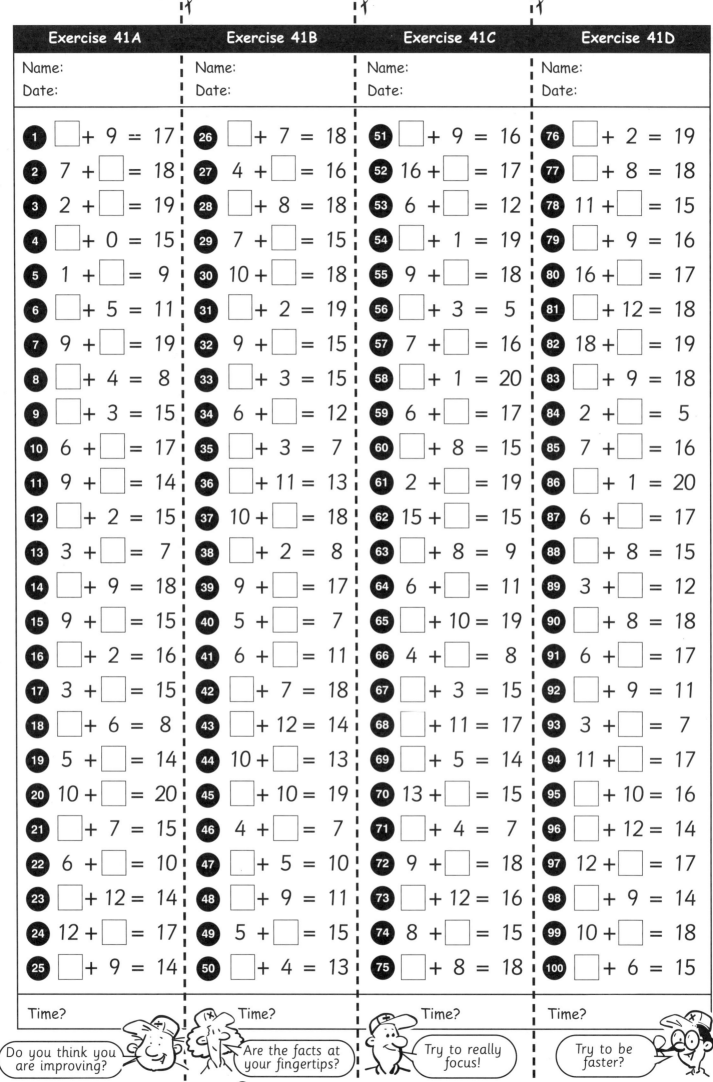

Do you think you are improving?

Are the facts at your fingertips?

Try to really focus!

Try to be faster?

Exercise 42A	Exercise 42B	Exercise 42C	Exercise 42D
Name:	Name:	Name:	Name:
Date:	Date:	Date:	Date:

1 $10 + \square = 14$
2 $\square + 1 = 18$
3 $9 + \square = 14$
4 $\square + 2 = 10$
5 $0 + \square = 3$
6 $\square + 1 = 13$
7 $2 + \square = 9$
8 $11 + \square = 15$
9 $\square + 9 = 11$
10 $10 + \square = 20$
11 $\square + 10 = 15$
12 $12 + \square = 18$
13 $\square + 2 = 5$
14 $\square + 0 = 9$
15 $11 + \square = 19$
16 $\square + 9 = 18$
17 $3 + \square = 5$
18 $6 + \square = 11$
19 $\square + 1 = 2$
20 $11 + \square = 20$
21 $\square + 9 = 17$
22 $2 + \square = 14$
23 $8 + \square = 16$
24 $\square + 3 = 16$
25 $9 + \square = 14$

26 $\square + 9 = 20$
27 $14 + \square = 16$
28 $2 + \square = 15$
29 $\square + 7 = 14$
30 $6 + \square = 13$
31 $\square + 9 = 19$
32 $11 + \square = 17$
33 $\square + 2 = 6$
34 $6 + \square = 12$
35 $\square + 0 = 8$
36 $\square + 12 = 17$
37 $10 + \square = 13$
38 $11 + \square = 19$
39 $\square + 1 = 7$
40 $2 + \square = 15$
41 $\square + 5 = 10$
42 $12 + \square = 18$
43 $1 + \square = 6$
44 $\square + 10 = 20$
45 $0 + \square = 19$
46 $\square + 1 = 14$
47 $9 + \square = 17$
48 $\square + 11 = 17$
49 $\square + 10 = 14$
50 $12 + \square = 13$

51 $12 + \square = 14$
52 $2 + \square = 8$
53 $\square + 9 = 10$
54 $8 + \square = 19$
55 $\square + 11 = 16$
56 $\square + 4 = 6$
57 $12 + \square = 14$
58 $\square + 1 = 12$
59 $9 + \square = 18$
60 $\square + 10 = 11$
61 $11 + \square = 17$
62 $9 + \square = 10$
63 $\square + 2 = 6$
64 $12 + \square = 14$
65 $\square + 0 = 15$
66 $1 + \square = 17$
67 $10 + \square = 19$
68 $\square + 11 = 14$
69 $8 + \square = 16$
70 $2 + \square = 4$
71 $\square + 10 = 17$
72 $6 + \square = 12$
73 $\square + 12 = 13$
74 $6 + \square = 11$
75 $\square + 1 = 20$

76 $\square + 1 = 7$
77 $9 + \square = 10$
78 $\square + 11 = 15$
79 $1 + \square = 18$
80 $\square + 2 = 7$
81 $12 + \square = 18$
82 $0 + \square = 9$
83 $\square + 11 = 13$
84 $9 + \square = 17$
85 $\square + 12 = 15$
86 $\square + 1 = 9$
87 $2 + \square = 4$
88 $\square + 12 = 16$
89 $10 + \square = 18$
90 $11 + \square = 14$
91 $\square + 9 = 10$
92 $2 + \square = 2$
93 $\square + 7 = 14$
94 $11 + \square = 13$
95 $\square + 0 = 7$
96 $\square + 10 = 12$
97 $12 + \square = 15$
98 $\square + 2 = 8$
99 $9 + \square = 17$
100 $\square + 11 = 14$

Time?	Time?	Time?	Time?

What is your time?   How did you do?   Is this your fastest time?   Did you reach your target?

Exercise 43A	Exercise 43B	Exercise 43C	Exercise 43D
Name:	Name:	Name:	Name:
Date:	Date:	Date:	Date:

1 $7 + \square = 18$ **26** $4 + \square = 7$ **51** $\square + 4 = 8$ **76** $6 + \square = 15$

2 $\square + 2 = 17$ **27** $\square + 8 = 16$ **52** $9 + \square = 14$ **77** $2 + \square = 5$

3 $8 + \square = 15$ **28** $11 + \square = 18$ **53** $\square + 2 = 15$ **78** $\square + 5 = 11$

4 $\square + 2 = 14$ **29** $4 + \square = 11$ **54** $2 + \square = 18$ **79** $2 + \square = 13$

5 $10 + \square = 20$ **30** $\square + 4 = 18$ **55** $13 + \square = 14$ **80** $\square + 5 = 14$

6 $5 + \square = 14$ **31** $5 + \square = 7$ **56** $\square + 9 = 18$ **81** $3 + \square = 11$

7 $\square + 2 = 8$ **32** $\square + 12 = 13$ **57** $9 + \square = 15$ **82** $\square + 12 = 18$

8 $4 + \square = 11$ **33** $6 + \square = 18$ **58** $\square + 6 = 11$ **83** $15 + \square = 19$

9 $5 + \square = 14$ **34** $3 + \square = 12$ **59** $5 + \square = 10$ **84** $\square + 1 = 11$

10 $\square + 10 = 20$ **35** $\square + 6 = 15$ **60** $12 + \square = 19$ **85** $11 + \square = 18$

11 $\square + 2 = 14$ **36** $12 + \square = 15$ **61** $\square + 7 = 12$ **86** $\square + 2 = 14$

12 $8 + \square = 15$ **37** $\square + 7 = 12$ **62** $3 + \square = 12$ **87** $3 + \square = 12$

13 $\square + 2 = 19$ **38** $13 + \square = 16$ **63** $10 + \square = 18$ **88** $10 + \square = 20$

14 $5 + \square = 19$ **39** $\square + 6 = 15$ **64** $\square + 17 = 18$ **89** $\square + 2 = 14$

15 $\square + 6 = 15$ **40** $5 + \square = 19$ **65** $6 + \square = 17$ **90** $8 + \square = 15$

16 $13 + \square = 16$ **41** $\square + 2 = 19$ **66** $\square + 7 = 11$ **91** $\square + 2 = 19$

17 $\square + 3 = 9$ **42** $8 + \square = 15$ **67** $2 + \square = 14$ **92** $5 + \square = 19$

18 $12 + \square = 15$ **43** $\square + 2 = 14$ **68** $\square + 9 = 11$ **93** $\square + 6 = 15$

19 $\square + 7 = 18$ **44** $10 + \square = 20$ **69** $6 + \square = 14$ **94** $13 + \square = 16$

20 $\square + 4 = 17$ **45** $\square + 9 = 13$ **70** $3 + \square = 17$ **95** $\square + 7 = 12$

21 $5 + \square = 7$ **46** $2 + \square = 8$ **71** $\square + 11 = 14$ **96** $12 + \square = 15$

22 $\square + 6 = 15$ **47** $2 + \square = 15$ **72** $8 + \square = 12$ **97** $\square + 6 = 15$

23 $7 + \square = 14$ **48** $\square + 8 = 14$ **73** $\square + 4 = 8$ **98** $1 + \square = 13$

24 $\square + 1 = 20$ **49** $14 + \square = 16$ **74** $\square + 5 = 14$ **99** $\square + 2 = 7$

25 $8 + \square = 15$ **50** $\square + 6 = 11$ **75** $3 + \square = 17$ **100** $\square + 4 = 18$

Time?	Time?	Time?	Time?

Which facts did you find the hardest?   Did you beat your target?   Can you try to be faster?   Where do you need to improve?

Exercise 44A	Exercise 44B	Exercise 44C	Exercise 44D
Name:	Name:	Name:	Name:
Date:	Date:	Date:	Date:

1 7 - 1 =	**26** 12 - 1 =	**51** 7 - 1 =	**76** 8 - 1 =
2 11 - 1 =	**27** 1 - 1 =	**52** 9 - 1 =	**77** 6 - 1 =
3 15 - 1 =	**28** 16 - 1 =	**53** 11 - 1 =	**78** 15 - 1 =
4 7 - 1 =	**29** 19 - 1 =	**54** 15 - 1 =	**79** 3 - 1 =
5 3 - 1 =	**30** 8 - 1 =	**55** 17 - 1 =	**80** 17 - 1 =
6 14 - 1 =	**31** 10 - 1 =	**56** 13 - 1 =	**81** 8 - 1 =
7 7 - 1 =	**32** 11 - 1 =	**57** 19 - 1 =	**82** 11 - 1 =
8 17 - 1 =	**33** 18 - 1 =	**58** 5 - 1 =	**83** 13 - 1 =
9 6 - 1 =	**34** 9 - 1 =	**59** 3 - 1 =	**84** 18 - 1 =
10 12 - 1 =	**35** 2 - 1 =	**60** 2 - 1 =	**85** 5 - 1 =
11 19 - 1 =	**36** 15 - 1 =	**61** 18 - 1 =	**86** 10 - 1 =
12 16 - 1 =	**37** 6 - 1 =	**62** 9 - 1 =	**87** 1 - 1 =
13 8 - 1 =	**38** 17 - 1 =	**63** 4 - 1 =	**88** 18 - 1 =
14 13 - 1 =	**39** 11 - 1 =	**64** 10 - 1 =	**89** 16 - 1 =
15 4 - 1 =	**40** 4 - 1 =	**65** 3 - 1 =	**90** 19 - 1 =
16 9 - 1 =	**41** 8 - 1 =	**66** 19 - 1 =	**91** 14 - 1 =
17 18 - 1 =	**42** 3 - 1 =	**67** 16 - 1 =	**92** 5 - 1 =
18 12 - 1 =	**43** 10 - 1 =	**68** 10 - 1 =	**93** 12 - 1 =
19 18 - 1 =	**44** 7 - 1 =	**69** 4 - 1 =	**94** 9 - 1 =
20 1 - 1 =	**45** 14 - 1 =	**70** 8 - 1 =	**95** 7 - 1 =
21 8 - 1 =	**46** 5 - 1 =	**71** 12 - 1 =	**96** 4 - 1 =
22 10 - 1 =	**47** 13 - 1 =	**72** 14 - 1 =	**97** 19 - 1 =
23 5 - 1 =	**48** 14 - 1 =	**73** 6 - 1 =	**98** 8 - 1 =
24 4 - 1 =	**49** 5 - 1 =	**74** 12 - 1 =	**99** 9 - 1 =
25 9 - 1 =	**50** 1 - 1 =	**75** 4 - 1 =	**100** 2 - 1 =

Time?	Time?	Time?	Time?
Is this your best score?	Have you reached your target?	Did you do well?	Do you think you are improving?

Exercise 45A	Exercise 45B	Exercise 45C	Exercise 45D
Name:	Name:	Name:	Name:
Date:	Date:	Date:	Date:

	Exercise 45A		Exercise 45B		Exercise 45C		Exercise 45D
1	$11 - 0 =$	26	$4 - 0 =$	51	$18 - 0 =$	76	$1 - 0 =$
2	$16 - 0 =$	27	$17 - 0 =$	52	$7 - 0 =$	77	$2 - 0 =$
3	$2 - 0 =$	28	$12 - 0 =$	53	$2 - 0 =$	78	$8 - 0 =$
4	$14 - 0 =$	29	$1 - 0 =$	54	$12 - 0 =$	79	$6 - 0 =$
5	$9 - 0 =$	30	$7 - 0 =$	55	$15 - 0 =$	80	$15 - 0 =$
6	$19 - 0 =$	31	$10 - 0 =$	56	$9 - 0 =$	81	$10 - 0 =$
7	$4 - 0 =$	32	$3 - 0 =$	57	$14 - 0 =$	82	$18 - 0 =$
8	$6 - 0 =$	33	$12 - 0 =$	58	$18 - 0 =$	83	$13 - 0 =$
9	$13 - 0 =$	34	$9 - 0 =$	59	$3 - 0 =$	84	$11 - 0 =$
10	$4 - 0 =$	35	$19 - 0 =$	60	$6 - 0 =$	85	$3 - 0 =$
11	$20 - 0 =$	36	$5 - 0 =$	61	$10 - 0 =$	86	$7 - 0 =$
12	$15 - 0 =$	37	$17 - 0 =$	62	$1 - 0 =$	87	$17 - 0 =$
13	$3 - 0 =$	38	$7 - 0 =$	63	$19 - 0 =$	88	$5 - 0 =$
14	$19 - 0 =$	39	$3 - 0 =$	64	$8 - 0 =$	89	$19 - 0 =$
15	$11 - 0 =$	40	$11 - 0 =$	65	$5 - 0 =$	90	$9 - 0 =$
16	$2 - 0 =$	41	$13 - 0 =$	66	$17 - 0 =$	91	$12 - 0 =$
17	$18 - 0 =$	42	$18 - 0 =$	67	$8 - 0 =$	92	$4 - 0 =$
18	$16 - 0 =$	43	$10 - 0 =$	68	$4 - 0 =$	93	$8 - 0 =$
19	$9 - 0 =$	44	$15 - 0 =$	69	$13 - 0 =$	94	$2 - 0 =$
20	$7 - 0 =$	45	$6 - 0 =$	70	$11 - 0 =$	95	$14 - 0 =$
21	$5 - 0 =$	46	$8 - 0 =$	71	$20 - 0 =$	96	$6 - 0 =$
22	$6 - 0 =$	47	$2 - 0 =$	72	$5 - 0 =$	97	$5 - 0 =$
23	$14 - 0 =$	48	$1 - 0 =$	73	$13 - 0 =$	98	$7 - 0 =$
24	$2 - 0 =$	49	$4 - 0 =$	74	$16 - 0 =$	99	$9 - 0 =$
25	$8 - 0 =$	50	$15 - 0 =$	75	$4 - 0 =$	100	$16 - 0 =$

Time?	Time?	Time?	Time?
Try to concentrate even more!	How do you think you are doing?	What have you learnt today?	How could you recall these facts even quicker?

Exercise 46A	Exercise 46B	Exercise 46C	Exercise 46D
Name:	Name:	Name:	Name:
Date:	Date:	Date:	Date:

1 19 - 10 =	**26** 13 - 10 =	**51** 18 - 10 =	**76** 14 - 10 =
2 11 - 10 =	**27** 17 - 10 =	**52** 11 - 10 =	**77** 15 - 10 =
3 16 - 10 =	**28** 14 - 10 =	**53** 14 - 10 =	**78** 17 - 10 =
4 18 - 10 =	**29** 19 - 10 =	**54** 12 - 10 =	**79** 19 - 10 =
5 13 - 10 =	**30** 11 - 10 =	**55** 14 - 10 =	**80** 12 - 10 =
6 17 - 10 =	**31** 16 - 10 =	**56** 20 - 10 =	**81** 18 - 10 =
7 20 - 10 =	**32** 20 - 10 =	**57** 12 - 10 =	**82** 16 - 10 =
8 15 - 10 =	**33** 13 - 10 =	**58** 16 - 10 =	**83** 14 - 10 =
9 19 - 10 =	**34** 12 - 10 =	**59** 13 - 10 =	**84** 20 - 10 =
10 12 - 10 =	**35** 18 - 10 =	**60** 15 - 10 =	**85** 17 - 10 =
11 11 - 10 =	**36** 20 - 10 =	**61** 13 - 10 =	**86** 12 - 10 =
12 18 - 10 =	**37** 15 - 10 =	**62** 20 - 10 =	**87** 15 - 10 =
13 10 - 10 =	**38** 14 - 10 =	**63** 19 - 10 =	**88** 13 - 10 =
14 20 - 10 =	**39** 18 - 10 =	**64** 17 - 10 =	**89** 18 - 10 =
15 12 - 10 =	**40** 12 - 10 =	**65** 15 - 10 =	**90** 12 - 10 =
16 14 - 10 =	**41** 13 - 10 =	**66** 13 - 10 =	**91** 11 - 10 =
17 15 - 10 =	**42** 17 - 10 =	**67** 16 - 10 =	**92** 17 - 10 =
18 17 - 10 =	**43** 15 - 10 =	**68** 10 - 10 =	**93** 14 - 10 =
19 14 - 10 =	**44** 19 - 10 =	**69** 12 - 10 =	**94** 18 - 10 =
20 15 - 10 =	**45** 13 - 10 =	**70** 19 - 10 =	**95** 12 - 10 =
21 19 - 10 =	**46** 15 - 10 =	**71** 16 - 10 =	**96** 13 - 10 =
22 13 - 10 =	**47** 18 - 10 =	**72** 13 - 10 =	**97** 16 - 10 =
23 16 - 10 =	**48** 19 - 10 =	**73** 17 - 10 =	**98** 20 - 10 =
24 20 - 10 =	**49** 14 - 10 =	**74** 16 - 10 =	**99** 16 - 10 =
25 15 - 10 =	**50** 16 - 10 =	**75** 15 - 10 =	**100** 19 - 10 =

Time?	Time?	Time?	Time?

Are the facts at your fingertips?   Try to really focus!   Which facts do you find the easiest?   Did you do well?

Exercise 47A	Exercise 47B	Exercise 47C	Exercise 47D
Name:	Name:	Name:	Name:
Date:	Date:	Date:	Date:

1 $6 - 2 =$	**26** $5 - 2 =$	**51** $14 - 2 =$	**76** $16 - 2 =$
2 $8 - 2 =$	**27** $10 - 2 =$	**52** $7 - 2 =$	**77** $7 - 2 =$
3 $9 - 2 =$	**28** $14 - 2 =$	**53** $15 - 2 =$	**78** $9 - 2 =$
4 $4 - 2 =$	**29** $13 - 2 =$	**54** $16 - 2 =$	**79** $4 - 2 =$
5 $5 - 2 =$	**30** $8 - 2 =$	**55** $18 - 2 =$	**80** $7 - 2 =$
6 $12 - 2 =$	**31** $15 - 2 =$	**56** $10 - 2 =$	**81** $13 - 2 =$
7 $10 - 2 =$	**32** $16 - 2 =$	**57** $15 - 2 =$	**82** $17 - 2 =$
8 $18 - 2 =$	**33** $13 - 2 =$	**58** $5 - 2 =$	**83** $4 - 2 =$
9 $16 - 2 =$	**34** $14 - 2 =$	**59** $9 - 2 =$	**84** $8 - 2 =$
10 $14 - 2 =$	**35** $4 - 2 =$	**60** $5 - 2 =$	**85** $15 - 2 =$
11 $12 - 2 =$	**36** $18 - 2 =$	**61** $9 - 2 =$	**86** $5 - 2 =$
12 $3 - 2 =$	**37** $20 - 2 =$	**62** $15 - 2 =$	**87** $10 - 2 =$
13 $16 - 2 =$	**38** $12 - 2 =$	**63** $13 - 2 =$	**88** $14 - 2 =$
14 $9 - 2 =$	**39** $5 - 2 =$	**64** $11 - 2 =$	**89** $13 - 2 =$
15 $12 - 2 =$	**40** $13 - 2 =$	**65** $17 - 2 =$	**90** $8 - 2 =$
16 $4 - 2 =$	**41** $14 - 2 =$	**66** $8 - 2 =$	**91** $15 - 2 =$
17 $17 - 2 =$	**42** $6 - 2 =$	**67** $13 - 2 =$	**92** $16 - 2 =$
18 $13 - 2 =$	**43** $10 - 2 =$	**68** $9 - 2 =$	**93** $19 - 2 =$
19 $11 - 2 =$	**44** $12 - 2 =$	**69** $5 - 2 =$	**94** $12 - 2 =$
20 $17 - 2 =$	**45** $14 - 2 =$	**70** $12 - 2 =$	**95** $9 - 2 =$
21 $13 - 2 =$	**46** $17 - 2 =$	**71** $13 - 2 =$	**96** $5 - 2 =$
22 $4 - 2 =$	**47** $15 - 2 =$	**72** $9 - 2 =$	**97** $18 - 2 =$
23 $8 - 2 =$	**48** $19 - 2 =$	**73** $18 - 2 =$	**98** $14 - 2 =$
24 $15 - 2 =$	**49** $7 - 2 =$	**74** $11 - 2 =$	**99** $6 - 2 =$
25 $3 - 2 =$	**50** $17 - 2 =$	**75** $14 - 2 =$	**100** $12 - 2 =$

Time?	Time?	Time?	Time?

Did you beat you score?

Which facts do you find the hardest?

Is this your best score?

Try to concentrate even more?

Exercise 48A	Exercise 48B	Exercise 48C	Exercise 48D
Name:	Name:	Name:	Name:
Date:	Date:	Date:	Date:

1 18 - 11 =	**26** 13 - 11 =	**51** 20 - 11 =	**76** 14 - 11 =
2 15 - 11 =	**27** 16 - 11 =	**52** 19 - 11 =	**77** 16 - 11 =
3 12 - 11 =	**28** 12 - 11 =	**53** 15 - 11 =	**78** 20 - 11 =
4 19 - 11 =	**29** 20 - 11 =	**54** 14 - 11 =	**79** 16 - 11 =
5 18 - 11 =	**30** 15 - 11 =	**55** 16 - 11 =	**80** 18 - 11 =
6 13 - 11 =	**31** 20 - 11 =	**56** 19 - 11 =	**81** 13 - 11 =
7 17 - 11 =	**32** 17 - 11 =	**57** 14 - 11 =	**82** 14 - 11 =
8 14 - 11 =	**33** 15 - 11 =	**58** 15 - 11 =	**83** 17 - 11 =
9 16 - 11 =	**34** 13 - 11 =	**59** 12 - 11 =	**84** 12 - 11 =
10 20 - 11 =	**35** 18 - 11 =	**60** 19 - 11 =	**85** 19 - 11 =
11 18 - 11 =	**36** 12 - 11 =	**61** 15 - 11 =	**86** 15 - 11 =
12 17 - 11 =	**37** 19 - 11 =	**62** 20 - 11 =	**87** 20 - 11 =
13 20 - 11 =	**38** 13 - 11 =	**63** 13 - 11 =	**88** 17 - 11 =
14 12 - 11 =	**39** 16 - 11 =	**64** 15 - 11 =	**89** 19 - 11 =
15 15 - 11 =	**40** 19 - 11 =	**65** 12 - 11 =	**90** 11 - 11 =
16 19 - 11 =	**41** 17 - 11 =	**66** 17 - 11 =	**91** 20 - 11 =
17 18 - 11 =	**42** 14 - 11 =	**67** 19 - 11 =	**92** 15 - 11 =
18 15 - 11 =	**43** 20 - 11 =	**68** 13 - 11 =	**93** 13 - 11 =
19 13 - 11 =	**44** 17 - 11 =	**69** 16 - 11 =	**94** 18 - 11 =
20 17 - 11 =	**45** 15 - 11 =	**70** 19 - 11 =	**95** 16 - 11 =
21 20 - 11 =	**46** 18 - 11 =	**71** 17 - 11 =	**96** 19 - 11 =
22 14 - 11 =	**47** 16 - 11 =	**72** 14 - 11 =	**97** 17 - 11 =
23 16 - 11 =	**48** 15 - 11 =	**73** 20 - 11 =	**98** 14 - 11 =
24 16 - 11 =	**49** 18 - 11 =	**74** 17 - 11 =	**99** 20 - 11 =
25 18 - 11 =	**50** 12 - 11 =	**75** 15 - 11 =	**100** 12 - 11 =

Time?	Time?	Time?	Time?

Is this your best score yet?

Did you beat your target?

Have you reached your target yet?

How do you think you are doing?

Exercise 49A	Exercise 49B	Exercise 49C	Exercise 49D
Name:	Name:	Name:	Name:
Date:	Date:	Date:	Date:

1 $15 - 12 =$	**26** $17 - 12 =$	**51** $20 - 12 =$	**76** $16 - 12 =$
2 $18 - 12 =$	**27** $15 - 12 =$	**52** $18 - 12 =$	**77** $19 - 12 =$
3 $20 - 12 =$	**28** $20 - 12 =$	**53** $14 - 12 =$	**78** $15 - 12 =$
4 $19 - 12 =$	**29** $13 - 12 =$	**54** $16 - 12 =$	**79** $17 - 12 =$
5 $13 - 12 =$	**30** $18 - 12 =$	**55** $17 - 12 =$	**80** $12 - 12 =$
6 $18 - 12 =$	**31** $16 - 12 =$	**56** $13 - 12 =$	**81** $19 - 12 =$
7 $15 - 12 =$	**32** $20 - 12 =$	**57** $19 - 12 =$	**82** $17 - 12 =$
8 $19 - 12 =$	**33** $14 - 12 =$	**58** $16 - 12 =$	**83** $20 - 12 =$
9 $18 - 12 =$	**34** $15 - 12 =$	**59** $18 - 12 =$	**84** $18 - 12 =$
10 $17 - 12 =$	**35** $17 - 12 =$	**60** $20 - 12 =$	**85** $16 - 12 =$
11 $20 - 12 =$	**36** $20 - 12 =$	**61** $17 - 12 =$	**86** $19 - 12 =$
12 $14 - 12 =$	**37** $16 - 12 =$	**62** $15 - 12 =$	**87** $13 - 12 =$
13 $18 - 12 =$	**38** $19 - 12 =$	**63** $18 - 12 =$	**88** $16 - 12 =$
14 $16 - 12 =$	**39** $15 - 12 =$	**64** $13 - 12 =$	**89** $20 - 12 =$
15 $19 - 12 =$	**40** $17 - 12 =$	**65** $20 - 12 =$	**90** $14 - 12 =$
16 $13 - 12 =$	**41** $12 - 12 =$	**66** $15 - 12 =$	**91** $17 - 12 =$
17 $17 - 12 =$	**42** $19 - 12 =$	**67** $17 - 12 =$	**92** $20 - 12 =$
18 $16 - 12 =$	**43** $15 - 12 =$	**68** $15 - 12 =$	**93** $16 - 12 =$
19 $14 - 12 =$	**44** $13 - 12 =$	**69** $20 - 12 =$	**94** $19 - 12 =$
20 $18 - 12 =$	**45** $18 - 12 =$	**70** $13 - 12 =$	**95** $15 - 12 =$
21 $20 - 12 =$	**46** $13 - 12 =$	**71** $18 - 12 =$	**96** $12 - 12 =$
22 $13 - 12 =$	**47** $16 - 12 =$	**72** $16 - 12 =$	**97** $18 - 12 =$
23 $16 - 12 =$	**48** $19 - 12 =$	**73** $20 - 12 =$	**98** $16 - 12 =$
24 $19 - 12 =$	**49** $17 - 12 =$	**74** $14 - 12 =$	**99** $17 - 12 =$
25 $18 - 12 =$	**50** $14 - 12 =$	**75** $17 - 12 =$	**100** $13 - 12 =$

Time?	Time?	Time?	Time?

Try to be even quicker next time!

Can you try to be faster?

Did you do well?

What have you learnt today?

Exercise 50A	Exercise 50B	Exercise 50C	Exercise 50D
Name:	Name:	Name:	Name:
Date:	Date:	Date:	Date:

1 16 - 9 =	**26** 14 - 9 =	**51** 15 - 9 =	**76** 13 - 9 =
2 20 - 9 =	**27** 17 - 9 =	**52** 18 - 9 =	**77** 19 - 9 =
3 18 - 9 =	**28** 16 - 9 =	**53** 13 - 9 =	**78** 17 - 9 =
4 13 - 9 =	**29** 14 - 9 =	**54** 12 - 9 =	**79** 14 - 9 =
5 16 - 9 =	**30** 11 - 9 =	**55** 10 - 9 =	**80** 12 - 9 =
6 14 - 9 =	**31** 10 - 9 =	**56** 17 - 9 =	**81** 20 - 9 =
7 18 - 9 =	**32** 20 - 9 =	**57** 20 - 9 =	**82** 18 - 9 =
8 10 - 9 =	**33** 12 - 9 =	**58** 16 - 9 =	**83** 13 - 9 =
9 15 - 9 =	**34** 17 - 9 =	**59** 14 - 9 =	**84** 16 - 9 =
10 17 - 9 =	**35** 15 - 9 =	**60** 11 - 9 =	**85** 14 - 9 =
11 20 - 9 =	**36** 12 - 9 =	**61** 15 - 9 =	**86** 10 - 9 =
12 16 - 9 =	**37** 18 - 9 =	**62** 19 - 9 =	**87** 15 - 9 =
13 11 - 9 =	**38** 14 - 9 =	**63** 16 - 9 =	**88** 17 - 9 =
14 19 - 9 =	**39** 12 - 9 =	**64** 17 - 9 =	**89** 20 - 9 =
15 16 - 9 =	**40** 16 - 9 =	**65** 20 - 9 =	**90** 11 - 9 =
16 11 - 9 =	**41** 14 - 9 =	**66** 10 - 9 =	**91** 19 - 9 =
17 18 - 9 =	**42** 10 - 9 =	**67** 17 - 9 =	**92** 16 - 9 =
18 12 - 9 =	**43** 13 - 9 =	**68** 12 - 9 =	**93** 12 - 9 =
19 14 - 9 =	**44** 19 - 9 =	**69** 15 - 9 =	**94** 18 - 9 =
20 19 - 9 =	**45** 17 - 9 =	**70** 19 - 9 =	**95** 14 - 9 =
21 16 - 9 =	**46** 18 - 9 =	**71** 16 - 9 =	**96** 19 - 9 =
22 13 - 9 =	**47** 14 - 9 =	**72** 20 - 9 =	**97** 12 - 9 =
23 17 - 9 =	**48** 12 - 9 =	**73** 15 - 9 =	**98** 14 - 9 =
24 11 - 9 =	**49** 20 - 9 =	**74** 18 - 9 =	**99** 18 - 9 =
25 18 - 9 =	**50** 17 - 9 =	**75** 16 - 9 =	**100** 12 - 9 =

Time?	Time?	Time?	Time?
Did you use strategies?	Where can you improve?	Are you improving?	Did you do well?

Exercise 51A	Exercise 51B	Exercise 51C	Exercise 51D
Name:	Name:	Name:	Name:
Date:	Date:	Date:	Date:

1	$17 - 7 =$	26	$3 - 3 =$	51	$8 - 8 =$	76	$9 - 8 =$
2	$4 - 4 =$	27	$13 - 3 =$	52	$13 - 12 =$	77	$7 - 7 =$
3	$15 - 14 =$	28	$19 - 19 =$	53	$17 - 7 =$	78	$12 - 11 =$
4	$17 - 16 =$	29	$12 - 2 =$	54	$14 - 14 =$	79	$18 - 18 =$
5	$13 - 13 =$	30	$20 - 10 =$	55	$10 - 9 =$	80	$20 - 19 =$
6	$18 - 8 =$	31	$14 - 13 =$	56	$12 - 2 =$	81	$15 - 5 =$
7	$11 - 10 =$	32	$18 - 17 =$	57	$7 - 6 =$	82	$9 - 8 =$
8	$19 - 19 =$	33	$7 - 7 =$	58	$15 - 14 =$	83	$6 - 6 =$
9	$7 - 6 =$	34	$13 - 3 =$	59	$2 - 2 =$	84	$19 - 18 =$
10	$12 - 12 =$	35	$16 - 15 =$	60	$11 - 1 =$	85	$16 - 6 =$
11	$14 - 4 =$	36	$3 - 3 =$	61	$19 - 19 =$	86	$8 - 7 =$
12	$12 - 11 =$	37	$8 - 7 =$	62	$12 - 11 =$	87	$2 - 2 =$
13	$20 - 20 =$	38	$1 - 1 =$	63	$7 - 6 =$	88	$18 - 17 =$
14	$12 - 2 =$	39	$19 - 9 =$	64	$8 - 8 =$	89	$14 - 14 =$
15	$17 - 7 =$	40	$14 - 4 =$	65	$13 - 12 =$	90	$19 - 9 =$
16	$9 - 8 =$	41	$17 - 17 =$	66	$4 - 4 =$	91	$11 - 10 =$
17	$17 - 17 =$	42	$2 - 2 =$	67	$13 - 3 =$	92	$13 - 13 =$
18	$20 - 19 =$	43	$19 - 18 =$	68	$15 - 14 =$	93	$12 - 2 =$
19	$4 - 4 =$	44	$13 - 13 =$	69	$19 - 19 =$	94	$5 - 5 =$
20	$13 - 12 =$	45	$17 - 7 =$	70	$8 - 7 =$	95	$10 - 9 =$
21	$8 - 8 =$	46	$14 - 13 =$	71	$15 - 5 =$	96	$2 - 2 =$
22	$19 - 9 =$	47	$19 - 19 =$	72	$8 - 8 =$	97	$17 - 7 =$
23	$14 - 4 =$	48	$15 - 14 =$	73	$14 - 13 =$	98	$11 - 10 =$
24	$10 - 9 =$	49	$18 - 8 =$	74	$6 - 6 =$	99	$9 - 9 =$
25	$9 - 9 =$	50	$16 - 15 =$	75	$14 - 4 =$	100	$17 - 16 =$

Time?	Time?	Time?	Time?
How did you do?	Did you beat your best score?	Can you try to be faster?	Have you reached your target?

Exercise 52A	Exercise 52B	Exercise 52C	Exercise 52D
Name:	Name:	Name:	Name:
Date:	Date:	Date:	Date:

1 $8 - 6 =$	**26** $8 - 7 =$	**51** $7 - 4 =$	**76** $8 - 6 =$
2 $7 - 3 =$	**27** $5 - 3 =$	**52** $9 - 7 =$	**77** $5 - 4 =$
3 $9 - 3 =$	**28** $8 - 6 =$	**53** $6 - 6 =$	**78** $7 - 6 =$
4 $8 - 6 =$	**29** $8 - 4 =$	**54** $7 - 3 =$	**79** $9 - 8 =$
5 $9 - 4 =$	**30** $8 - 6 =$	**55** $7 - 6 =$	**80** $8 - 5 =$
6 $8 - 7 =$	**31** $9 - 7 =$	**56** $6 - 4 =$	**81** $6 - 3 =$
7 $7 - 5 =$	**32** $4 - 3 =$	**57** $8 - 7 =$	**82** $8 - 7 =$
8 $9 - 8 =$	**33** $7 - 6 =$	**58** $6 - 5 =$	**83** $6 - 5 =$
9 $8 - 3 =$	**34** $8 - 7 =$	**59** $9 - 8 =$	**84** $6 - 4 =$
10 $8 - 7 =$	**35** $8 - 4 =$	**60** $8 - 3 =$	**85** $9 - 7 =$
11 $7 - 5 =$	**36** $8 - 6 =$	**61** $6 - 6 =$	**86** $7 - 5 =$
12 $8 - 4 =$	**37** $7 - 3 =$	**62** $9 - 7 =$	**87** $7 - 3 =$
13 $9 - 8 =$	**38** $6 - 6 =$	**63** $5 - 4 =$	**88** $8 - 7 =$
14 $6 - 3 =$	**39** $5 - 5 =$	**64** $6 - 6 =$	**89** $6 - 4 =$
15 $9 - 7 =$	**40** $8 - 7 =$	**65** $7 - 5 =$	**90** $5 - 4 =$
16 $7 - 4 =$	**41** $4 - 4 =$	**66** $8 - 7 =$	**91** $8 - 6 =$
17 $8 - 7 =$	**42** $9 - 8 =$	**67** $4 - 3 =$	**92** $5 - 5 =$
18 $7 - 5 =$	**43** $6 - 3 =$	**68** $9 - 7 =$	**93** $9 - 8 =$
19 $5 - 3 =$	**44** $9 - 7 =$	**69** $6 - 4 =$	**94** $7 - 3 =$
20 $9 - 7 =$	**45** $6 - 5 =$	**70** $8 - 6 =$	**95** $8 - 6 =$
21 $6 - 4 =$	**46** $7 - 4 =$	**71** $8 - 5 =$	**96** $9 - 7 =$
22 $6 - 6 =$	**47** $7 - 3 =$	**72** $8 - 3 =$	**97** $6 - 4 =$
23 $8 - 3 =$	**48** $8 - 7 =$	**73** $8 - 7 =$	**98** $7 - 6 =$
24 $8 - 7 =$	**49** $7 - 6 =$	**74** $9 - 7 =$	**99** $6 - 5 =$
25 $5 - 5 =$	**50** $8 - 4 =$	**75** $4 - 4 =$	**100** $6 - 4 =$

Time?	Time?	Time?	Time?

How do you think you are doing?

How did you do?

Is this your best score?

Which facts do you find the easiest?

Exercise 53A	Exercise 53B	Exercise 53C	Exercise 53D
Name:	Name:	Name:	Name:
Date:	Date:	Date:	Date:

1	19 - 14 =	**26**	18 - 17 =	**51**	18 - 14 =	**76**	18 - 15 =
2	18 - 16 =	**27**	14 - 13 =	**52**	19 - 17 =	**77**	16 - 14 =
3	17 - 13 =	**28**	19 - 17 =	**53**	14 - 13 =	**78**	19 - 17 =
4	15 - 12 =	**29**	16 - 14 =	**54**	17 - 16 =	**79**	14 - 13 =
5	18 - 15 =	**30**	18 - 16 =	**55**	18 - 17 =	**80**	19 - 15 =
6	19 - 18 =	**31**	18 - 15 =	**56**	18 - 14 =	**81**	18 - 17 =
7	18 - 14 =	**32**	18 - 13 =	**57**	18 - 16 =	**82**	17 - 15 =
8	19 - 17 =	**33**	18 - 17 =	**58**	17 - 13 =	**83**	16 - 16 =
9	17 - 14 =	**34**	19 - 17 =	**59**	16 - 16 =	**84**	15 - 14 =
10	19 - 12 =	**35**	14 - 14 =	**60**	15 - 15 =	**85**	19 - 17 =
11	16 - 16 =	**36**	16 - 14 =	**61**	18 - 17 =	**86**	16 - 16 =
12	15 - 13 =	**37**	15 - 14 =	**62**	14 - 14 =	**87**	18 - 13 =
13	17 - 16 =	**38**	18 - 16 =	**63**	19 - 18 =	**88**	19 - 18 =
14	16 - 14 =	**39**	15 - 15 =	**64**	16 - 13 =	**89**	16 - 15 =
15	18 - 17 =	**40**	19 - 18 =	**65**	19 - 17 =	**90**	18 - 17 =
16	19 - 13 =	**41**	17 - 13 =	**66**	16 - 15 =	**91**	16 - 14 =
17	16 - 15 =	**42**	18 - 16 =	**67**	17 - 14 =	**92**	17 - 16 =
18	19 - 18 =	**43**	19 - 17 =	**68**	17 - 13 =	**93**	17 - 14 =
19	18 - 13 =	**44**	16 - 14 =	**69**	18 - 17 =	**94**	19 - 18 =
20	16 - 16 =	**45**	17 - 16 =	**70**	17 - 16 =	**95**	18 - 15 =
21	19 - 17 =	**46**	16 - 15 =	**71**	18 - 14 =	**96**	16 - 13 =
22	15 - 14 =	**47**	16 - 14 =	**72**	14 - 14 =	**97**	18 - 17 =
23	15 - 11 =	**48**	18 - 17 =	**73**	19 - 17 =	**98**	16 - 15 =
24	16 - 16 =	**49**	15 - 13 =	**74**	18 - 17 =	**99**	19 - 17 =
25	17 - 15 =	**50**	18 - 16 =	**75**	18 - 13 =	**100**	18 - 14 =

Time?	Time?	Time?	Time?

How did you do?

Have you reached your target?

Try to be faster?

What is your time?

Exercise 54A	Exercise 54B	Exercise 54C	Exercise 54D
Name:	Name:	Name:	Name:
Date:	Date:	Date:	Date:
1 17 - 3 =	**26** 16 - 4 =	**51** 18 - 5 =	**76** 14 - 5 =
2 13 - 4 =	**27** 19 - 8 =	**52** 14 - 7 =	**77** 19 - 6 =
3 16 - 7 =	**28** 14 - 3 =	**53** 19 - 4 =	**78** 14 - 4 =
4 14 - 5 =	**29** 11 - 7 =	**54** 16 - 5 =	**79** 19 - 7 =
5 13 - 8 =	**30** 17 - 5 =	**55** 18 - 7 =	**80** 18 - 3 =
6 19 - 6 =	**31** 12 - 4 =	**56** 17 - 3 =	**81** 17 - 7 =
7 17 - 3 =	**32** 14 - 3 =	**57** 19 - 5 =	**82** 19 - 5 =
8 18 - 5 =	**33** 18 - 7 =	**58** 14 - 8 =	**83** 15 - 6 =
9 15 - 6 =	**34** 17 - 6 =	**59** 16 - 6 =	**84** 14 - 7 =
10 16 - 4 =	**35** 16 - 4 =	**60** 17 - 4 =	**85** 15 - 6 =
11 14 - 4 =	**36** 19 - 7 =	**61** 19 - 6 =	**86** 18 - 3 =
12 19 - 7 =	**37** 16 - 6 =	**62** 16 - 7 =	**87** 19 - 8 =
13 18 - 6 =	**38** 12 - 3 =	**63** 13 - 4 =	**88** 16 - 5 =
14 14 - 3 =	**39** 14 - 6 =	**64** 16 - 6 =	**89** 17 - 7 =
15 19 - 7 =	**40** 19 - 4 =	**65** 18 - 5 =	**90** 18 - 4 =
16 18 - 7 =	**41** 14 - 7 =	**66** 15 - 8 =	**91** 14 - 3 =
17 16 - 3 =	**42** 18 - 5 =	**67** 16 - 3 =	**92** 19 - 6 =
18 18 - 6 =	**43** 15 - 8 =	**68** 17 - 6 =	**93** 18 - 7 =
19 17 - 7 =	**44** 17 - 3 =	**69** 18 - 7 =	**94** 15 - 4 =
20 19 - 4 =	**45** 18 - 6 =	**70** 14 - 4 =	**95** 18 - 7 =
21 18 - 6 =	**46** 14 - 7 =	**71** 19 - 6 =	**96** 16 - 3 =
22 16 - 3 =	**47** 19 - 4 =	**72** 16 - 5 =	**97** 19 - 6 =
23 19 - 6 =	**48** 16 - 6 =	**73** 18 - 4 =	**98** 14 - 4 =
24 14 - 5 =	**49** 14 - 5 =	**74** 17 - 7 =	**99** 13 - 6 =
25 18 - 7 =	**50** 18 - 7 =	**75** 18 - 3 =	**100** 17 - 8 =
Time?	Time?	Time?	Time?

What is your time?

How did you do?

Try to be faster?

Have you reached your target?

Exercise 55A	Exercise 55B	Exercise 55C	Exercise 55D
Name:	Name:	Name:	Name:
Date:	Date:	Date:	Date:

#	55A	#	55B	#	55C	#	55D
1	$11 - 0 =$	26	$13 - 0 =$	51	$19 - 1 =$	76	$18 - 0 =$
2	$16 - 10 =$	27	$14 - 10 =$	52	$15 - 10 =$	77	$16 - 10 =$
3	$1 + 10 =$	28	$14 - 1 =$	53	$8 + 10 =$	78	$13 - 1 =$
4	$15 - 1 =$	29	$2 + 10 =$	54	$12 - 0 =$	79	$19 + 1 =$
5	$14 + 0 =$	30	$7 - 0 =$	55	$10 + 6 =$	80	$17 - 10 =$
6	$20 - 10 =$	31	$1 + 5 =$	56	$19 - 10 =$	81	$11 + 0 =$
7	$1 - 0 =$	32	$18 - 10 =$	57	$13 - 10 =$	82	$6 - 0 =$
8	$5 + 10 =$	33	$7 - 1 =$	58	$6 + 1 =$	83	$19 - 10 =$
9	$13 - 10 =$	34	$0 + 3 =$	59	$3 - 0 =$	84	$7 + 10 =$
10	$1 + 8 =$	35	$8 - 0 =$	60	$0 + 16 =$	85	$12 - 10 =$
11	$10 - 0 =$	36	$1 + 2 =$	61	$12 - 1 =$	86	$10 + 8 =$
12	$16 + 0 =$	37	$12 - 10 =$	62	$7 + 10 =$	87	$4 - 1 =$
13	$12 - 10 =$	38	$10 + 1 =$	63	$15 - 10 =$	88	$5 + 1 =$
14	$7 - 1 =$	39	$11 - 0 =$	64	$5 - 0 =$	89	$8 - 0 =$
15	$4 + 10 =$	40	$13 - 10 =$	65	$10 + 9 =$	90	$16 - 10 =$
16	$8 - 0 =$	41	$19 + 1 =$	66	$16 - 1 =$	91	$0 + 15 =$
17	$1 + 7 =$	42	$17 - 1 =$	67	$3 + 1 =$	92	$9 - 1 =$
18	$18 - 10 =$	43	$11 + 0 =$	68	$18 - 10 =$	93	$10 + 9 =$
19	$20 - 10 =$	44	$6 - 0 =$	69	$19 - 0 =$	94	$10 - 0 =$
20	$17 + 0 =$	45	$17 - 10 =$	70	$2 + 10 =$	95	$14 - 10 =$
21	$20 - 0 =$	46	$10 + 10 =$	71	$14 - 10 =$	96	$7 + 1 =$
22	$3 + 10 =$	47	$6 - 1 =$	72	$1 + 14 =$	97	$18 - 1 =$
23	$3 - 1 =$	48	$9 + 1 =$	73	$8 - 1 =$	98	$9 + 0 =$
24	$18 + 1 =$	49	$7 - 0 =$	74	$0 + 20 =$	99	$3 - 0 =$
25	$15 - 10 =$	50	$4 + 0 =$	75	$10 + 6 =$	100	$5 + 10 =$

Time?	Time?	Time?	Time?

Which facts did you find the hardest?

Did you beat your target?

Can you try to be faster?

Where do you need to improve?

Exercise 56A	Exercise 56B	Exercise 56C	Exercise 56D
Name:	Name:	Name:	Name:
Date:	Date:	Date:	Date:

#	56A	#	56B	#	56C	#	56D
1	6 - 2 =	26	18 - 10 =	51	16 - 1 =	76	18 - 10 =
2	12 - 10 =	27	10 - 9 =	52	18 - 10 =	77	20 - 10 =
3	1 + 5 =	28	14 - 2 =	53	2 + 10 =	78	6 - 2 =
4	18 - 10 =	29	5 + 0 =	54	7 - 2 =	79	17 + 0 =
5	0 + 3 =	30	15 - 10 =	55	1 + 14 =	80	20 - 1 =
6	8 - 0 =	31	7 + 10 =	56	8 - 1 =	81	3 + 10 =
7	13 - 10 =	32	12 - 1 =	57	18 - 10 =	82	3 - 1 =
8	2 + 8 =	33	3 - 0 =	58	11 + 2 =	83	15 - 10 =
9	11 - 0 =	34	0 + 16 =	59	20 - 0 =	84	10 + 2 =
10	19 + 1 =	35	13 - 10 =	60	10 + 6 =	85	7 - 1 =
11	17 - 1 =	36	10 + 6 =	61	16 - 2 =	86	16 + 0 =
12	6 + 0 =	37	3 - 2 =	62	8 + 2 =	87	10 - 0 =
13	18 - 2 =	38	12 + 2 =	63	16 - 10 =	88	14 + 2 =
14	17 - 10 =	39	12 - 0 =	64	13 - 1 =	89	8 - 1 =
15	10 + 10 =	40	19 - 1 =	65	19 + 1 =	90	13 - 10 =
16	6 - 1 =	41	7 + 2 =	66	17 - 10 =	91	5 + 10 =
17	9 + 1 =	42	15 - 10 =	67	11 + 0 =	92	18 - 2 =
18	7 - 0 =	43	8 + 10 =	68	8 - 2 =	93	14 + 0 =
19	7 - 2 =	44	19 - 1 =	69	6 - 0 =	94	15 - 1 =
20	4 + 0 =	45	18 - 0 =	70	9 + 10 =	95	7 - 1 =
21	8 - 1 =	46	11 + 2 =	71	12 - 10 =	96	0 + 3 =
22	16 + 2 =	47	16 - 10 =	72	3 + 2 =	97	7 - 2 =
23	14 - 10 =	48	19 + 1 =	73	4 - 1 =	98	1 + 2 =
24	1 + 14 =	49	17 - 10 =	74	5 + 1 =	99	8 - 0 =
25	19 - 0 =	50	11 + 0 =	75	0 + 15 =	100	0 + 3 =

Time?	Time?	Time?	Time?

Is this your best score?

Have you reached your target?

Did you do well?

Do you think you are improving?

Exercise 57A	Exercise 57B	Exercise 57C	Exercise 57D
Name:	Name:	Name:	Name:
Date:	Date:	Date:	Date:

1 $10 - 0 =$	**26** $16 - 10 =$	**51** $17 - 12 =$	**76** $7 - 2 =$
2 $18 - 11 =$	**27** $14 - 2 =$	**52** $15 - 10 =$	**77** $17 - 12 =$
3 $4 + 12 =$	**28** $18 - 12 =$	**53** $7 + 2 =$	**78** $8 - 0 =$
4 $8 - 1 =$	**29** $10 + 6 =$	**54** $19 - 1 =$	**79** $9 + 1 =$
5 $5 + 10 =$	**30** $20 - 0 =$	**55** $12 + 7 =$	**80** $16 - 11 =$
6 $16 - 12 =$	**31** $11 + 2 =$	**56** $19 - 11 =$	**81** $10 + 10 =$
7 $18 - 2 =$	**32** $18 - 10 =$	**57** $3 - 2 =$	**82** $14 - 12 =$
8 $14 + 0 =$	**33** $17 - 11 =$	**58** $9 + 11 =$	**83** $17 - 10 =$
9 $16 - 11 =$	**34** $1 + 14 =$	**59** $13 - 10 =$	**84** $8 + 11 =$
10 $15 + 1 =$	**35** $8 - 1 =$	**60** $10 + 6 =$	**85** $18 - 2 =$
11 $7 - 1 =$	**36** $5 + 12 =$	**61** $3 - 0 =$	**86** $6 + 0 =$
12 $4 + 12 =$	**37** $7 - 2 =$	**62** $7 + 10 =$	**87** $17 - 1 =$
13 $7 - 2 =$	**38** $2 + 10 =$	**63** $15 - 10 =$	**88** $4 + 1 =$
14 $8 - 0 =$	**39** $16 - 12 =$	**64** $12 - 11 =$	**89** $19 - 11 =$
15 $0 + 3 =$	**40** $18 - 10 =$	**65** $5 + 0 =$	**90** $11 - 0 =$
16 $19 - 12 =$	**41** $11 + 0 =$	**66** $14 - 2 =$	**91** $2 + 8 =$
17 $0 + 15 =$	**42** $17 - 10 =$	**67** $5 + 12 =$	**92** $11 - 10 =$
18 $14 - 11 =$	**43** $19 + 1 =$	**68** $10 - 9 =$	**93** $3 + 12 =$
19 $4 - 1 =$	**44** $20 - 11 =$	**69** $18 - 10 =$	**94** $8 - 0 =$
20 $3 + 2 =$	**45** $16 - 10 =$	**70** $19 + 0 =$	**95** $18 - 12 =$
21 $12 - 10 =$	**46** $11 + 2 =$	**71** $14 - 12 =$	**96** $0 + 3 =$
22 $7 + 11 =$	**47** $18 - 0 =$	**72** $1 + 14 =$	**97** $18 - 10 =$
23 $6 - 0 =$	**48** $3 + 11 =$	**73** $14 - 10 =$	**98** $1 + 5 =$
24 $9 + 10 =$	**49** $19 - 1 =$	**74** $16 + 2 =$	**99** $12 - 10 =$
25 $13 - 1 =$	**50** $8 + 10 =$	**75** $8 + 1 =$	**100** $6 + 2 =$

Time?	Time?	Time?	Time?
Try to concentrate even more!	How do you think you are doing?	What have you learnt today?	How could you recall these facts even quicker?

Exercise 58A	Exercise 58B	Exercise 58C	Exercise 58D
Name:	Name:	Name:	Name:
Date:	Date:	Date:	Date:

1 $20 - 0 =$	**26** $17 - 12 =$	**51** $16 - 8 =$	**76** $18 - 2 =$
2 $17 - 9 =$	**27** $15 - 10 =$	**52** $14 - 12 =$	**77** $16 - 8 =$
3 $11 + 2 =$	**28** $12 - 6 =$	**53** $1 + 13 =$	**78** $17 - 1 =$
4 $18 - 10 =$	**29** $7 + 2 =$	**54** $18 - 10 =$	**79** $8 + 8 =$
5 $1 + 14 =$	**30** $19 - 1 =$	**55** $16 + 2 =$	**80** $15 - 9 =$
6 $17 - 11 =$	**31** $10 + 5 =$	**56** $14 - 9 =$	**81** $4 + 1 =$
7 $14 - 7 =$	**32** $19 - 11 =$	**57** $8 - 1 =$	**82** $14 - 7 =$
8 $5 + 12 =$	**33** $13 - 9 =$	**58** $8 + 9 =$	**83** $19 - 11 =$
9 $7 - 2 =$	**34** $7 + 9 =$	**59** $14 - 7 =$	**84** $5 + 9 =$
10 $6 + 9 =$	**35** $3 - 2 =$	**60** $6 + 6 =$	**85** $11 - 0 =$
11 $18 - 10 =$	**36** $7 + 7 =$	**61** $7 - 2 =$	**86** $2 + 8 =$
12 $4 + 4 =$	**37** $13 - 10 =$	**62** $9 + 1 =$	**87** $12 - 6 =$
13 $12 - 9 =$	**38** $10 + 6 =$	**63** $8 - 0 =$	**88** $3 + 12 =$
14 $17 - 10 =$	**39** $3 - 0 =$	**64** $16 - 11 =$	**89** $11 - 10 =$
15 $19 + 1 =$	**40** $8 - 4 =$	**65** $4 + 4 =$	**90** $17 - 9 =$
16 $18 - 9 =$	**41** $4 + 9 =$	**66** $15 - 9 =$	**91** $0 + 3 =$
17 $16 + 0 =$	**42** $15 - 10 =$	**67** $10 + 10 =$	**92** $10 - 5 =$
18 $20 - 11 =$	**43** $5 + 5 =$	**68** $18 - 9 =$	**93** $1 + 6 =$
19 $18 - 0 =$	**44** $10 - 9 =$	**69** $14 - 12 =$	**94** $12 - 10 =$
20 $6 + 6 =$	**45** $12 - 11 =$	**70** $17 + 2 =$	**95** $8 - 1 =$
21 $19 - 1 =$	**46** $5 + 0 =$	**71** $16 - 9 =$	**96** $6 + 9 =$
22 $3 + 9 =$	**47** $14 - 2 =$	**72** $9 + 9 =$	**97** $12 - 6 =$
23 $12 - 6 =$	**48** $5 + 12 =$	**73** $8 - 4 =$	**98** $3 + 3 =$
24 $8 + 10 =$	**49** $10 - 5 =$	**74** $17 + 1 =$	**99** $6 - 3 =$
25 $11 - 9 =$	**50** $19 + 0 =$	**75** $5 + 9 =$	**100** $8 + 9 =$

Time?	Time?	Time?	Time?
Are the facts at your fingertips?	Try to really focus!	Which facts do you find the easiest?	Did you do well?

Exercise 59A	Exercise 59B	Exercise 59C	Exercise 59D
Name:	Name:	Name:	Name:
Date:	Date:	Date:	Date:

#	59A	#	59B	#	59C	#	59D
1	$14 - 7 =$	26	$17 - 3 =$	51	$14 - 7 =$	76	$10 - 5 =$
2	$19 - 4 =$	27	$11 - 6 =$	52	$19 - 5 =$	77	$18 - 4 =$
3	$7 + 7 =$	28	$15 - 3 =$	53	$3 + 12 =$	78	$19 - 9 =$
4	$14 - 2 =$	29	$1 + 1 =$	54	$20 - 5 =$	79	$7 + 8 =$
5	$13 + 3 =$	30	$2 - 1 =$	55	$6 + 6 =$	80	$17 - 3 =$
6	$15 - 7 =$	31	$7 + 8 =$	56	$14 - 4 =$	81	$16 + 3 =$
7	$20 - 5 =$	32	$19 - 4 =$	57	$7 - 4 =$	82	$12 - 6 =$
8	$3 + 4 =$	33	$15 - 7 =$	58	$8 + 9 =$	83	$18 - 9 =$
9	$13 - 2 =$	34	$2 + 12 =$	59	$16 - 3 =$	84	$14 + 5 =$
10	$4 + 4 =$	35	$15 - 3 =$	60	$5 + 15 =$	85	$18 - 4 =$
11	$19 - 4 =$	36	$8 + 8 =$	61	$19 - 4 =$	86	$6 + 6 =$
12	$7 + 8 =$	37	$13 - 11 =$	62	$12 + 3 =$	87	$15 - 2 =$
13	$8 - 4 =$	38	$3 + 4 =$	63	$10 - 5 =$	88	$6 + 7 =$
14	$15 - 3 =$	39	$14 - 2 =$	64	$17 - 3 =$	89	$20 - 5 =$
15	$9 + 9 =$	40	$6 - 3 =$	65	$7 + 7 =$	90	$15 - 7 =$
16	$20 - 5 =$	41	$14 + 4 =$	66	$19 - 4 =$	91	$13 + 4 =$
17	$15 + 4 =$	42	$19 - 4 =$	67	$4 + 5 =$	92	$16 - 8 =$
18	$18 - 9 =$	43	$14 + 5 =$	68	$18 - 4 =$	93	$5 + 5 =$
19	$9 - 4 =$	44	$11 - 6 =$	69	$16 - 3 =$	94	$15 - 2 =$
20	$3 + 3 =$	45	$16 - 8 =$	70	$2 + 2 =$	95	$16 - 3 =$
21	$14 - 2 =$	46	$5 + 5 =$	71	$4 - 2 =$	96	$4 + 5 =$
22	$13 + 2 =$	47	$16 - 3 =$	72	$4 + 15 =$	97	$15 - 8 =$
23	$20 - 15 =$	48	$6 + 7 =$	73	$19 - 4 =$	98	$14 + 4 =$
24	$6 + 7 =$	49	$18 - 4 =$	74	$12 + 3 =$	99	$15 - 2 =$
25	$6 - 3 =$	50	$12 + 2 =$	75	$14 + 5 =$	100	$12 + 2 =$

Time?	Time?	Time?	Time?

Did you beat your score?

Which facts do you find the hardest?

Is this your best score?

Try to concentrate even more!

Exercise 60A	Exercise 60B	Exercise 60C	Exercise 60D
Name:	Name:	Name:	Name:
Date:	Date:	Date:	Date:

1 14 - 7 =	**26** 15 - 2 =	**51** 19 - 4 =	**76** 12 - 6 =
2 20 - 0 =	**27** 11 - 6 =	**52** 15 - 7 =	**77** 15 - 9 =
3 7 + 7 =	**28** 18 - 7 =	**53** 16 + 2 =	**78** 19 - 9 =
4 19 - 4 =	**29** 14 + 4 =	**54** 17 - 3 =	**79** 16 + 3 =
5 11 + 2 =	**30** 15 - 8 =	**55** 16 + 3 =	**80** 14 - 7 =
6 14 - 2 =	**31** 4 + 5 =	**56** 2 - 1 =	**81** 6 + 6 =
7 18 - 10 =	**32** 16 - 11 =	**57** 14 - 9 =	**82** 18 - 4 =
8 3 + 14 =	**33** 8 - 0 =	**58** 16 + 2 =	**83** 10 - 5 =
9 7 - 2 =	**34** 12 + 3 =	**59** 18 - 10 =	**84** 7 + 7 =
10 4 + 4 =	**35** 19 - 4 =	**60** 1 + 13 =	**85** 8 - 0 =
11 19 - 4 =	**36** 5 + 15 =	**61** 4 - 3 =	**86** 2 + 2 =
12 4 + 4 =	**37** 14 - 7 =	**62** 16 + 2 =	**87** 19 - 4 =
13 12 - 9 =	**38** 8 + 9 =	**63** 14 - 9 =	**88** 10 + 10 =
14 17 - 10 =	**39** 8 - 1 =	**64** 8 - 1 =	**89** 18 - 9 =
15 9 + 9 =	**40** 14 - 9 =	**65** 8 - 9 =	**90** 14 - 12 =
16 20 - 5 =	**41** 8 + 9 =	**66** 15 - 3 =	**91** 14 + 5 =
17 16 + 0 =	**42** 7 - 4 =	**67** 8 + 8 =	**92** 11 - 6 =
18 20 - 11 =	**43** 6 + 6 =	**68** 8 - 0 =	**93** 2 + 2 =
19 18 - 9 =	**44** 3 - 0 =	**69** 18 - 4 =	**94** 8 - 1 =
20 3 + 3 =	**45** 8 - 4 =	**70** 2 + 2 =	**95** 15 - 7 =
21 19 - 1 =	**46** 7 + 7 =	**71** 14 - 12 =	**96** 1 + 6 =
22 13 + 2 =	**47** 19 - 4 =	**72** 5 + 5 =	**97** 10 - 5 =
23 12 - 6 =	**48** 6 + 6 =	**73** 10 - 9 =	**98** 3 + 3 =
24 6 + 7 =	**49** 14 - 7 =	**74** 3 + 12 =	**99** 15 - 8 =
25 11 - 9 =	**50** 7 + 8 =	**75** 17 + 3 =	**100** 8 + 9 =

Time?	Time?	Time?	Time?
Is this your best score yet?	Did you beat your target?	Have you reached your target yet?	How do you think you are doing?

Facts at your Fingertips

This is to certify that

can

Well done!

Signed (Teacher)

Date

TOPICAL RESOURCES